Test Your Idioms

Peter Watcyn-Jones

PENGUIN ENGLISH

Pearson Education Limited
Edinburgh Gate
Harlow
Essex CM20 2JE, England
and Associated Companies throughout the world.

ISBN 0 582 45173 6

First published 1990
This edition published 2002
Text copyright © Peter Watcyn-Jones 1990, 2000, 2002

Designed and typeset by Pantek Arts Ltd, Maidstone, Kent
Test Your format devised by Peter Watcyn-Jones
Illustrations by Phil Healey, Vince Silcock and Ross Thomson
Printed in Italy by Rotolito Lombarda

Acknowledgements
To Tina and the staff at Hollandia – Malmö and Sweden's best coffee bar.

Published by Pearson Education Limited in association with Penguin Books Ltd, both companies being subsidiaries of Pearson plc.

For a complete list of the titles available from Penguin English please visit our website at www.penguinenglish.com, or write to your local Pearson Education office or to: Marketing Department, Penguin Longman Publishing, 80 Strand, London WC2R 0RL.

Contents

To the student

What is an idiom?

An idiom is a group of words that has a completely different meaning from the meaning of each word on its own. So, for example, although you might know the words *storm* and *teacup* it would be almost impossible to guess the meaning of the idiom *a storm in a teacup*, which is a situation where people get very upset and angry over something that is unimportant, e.g. *Don't worry about this silly row with the boss – it's just a storm in a teacup*. Similarly, knowing the verb *to go* and the noun *song* won't really help you to understand the meaning of the idiom *to go for a song* which is when something is sold very cheaply, e.g. *As no one else at the auction seemed interested in the painting, it went for a song*. Idioms really have to be learnt as complete phrases, each with its own unique (often unexpected) meaning.

Test Your Idioms contains sixty tests covering over 900 of the most common and useful idioms in English. The book is divided into six sections:

- Idioms using adjectives
- Idioms using nouns
- Idioms using verbs
- Idioms using prepositions
- 'Special category' idioms
- 'Special topics' idioms.

To make the book more challenging and more fun, there is a wide variety of tests, ranging from matching idioms and definitions, multiple-choice exercises, crosswords, gap-filling exercises and true–false exercises where you have to decide whether an idiom is used correctly or not. In addition, useful notes are given after most tests, including hints on learning words, suggestions for other idioms that can be used, and notes on the origins of certain idioms. To further 'fix' the meaning of the idiom, wide use is made of drawings and cartoons. The last test in each section is intended as a revision exercise for that section.

A key is included at the back of the book which not only gives the correct answers but also, when not included in the actual test, gives a detailed explanation of each idiom.

It is hoped that students using this book will find the learning of idioms both stimulating and enjoyable.

Peter Watcyn-Jones

Section 1: Idioms using adjectives

This section looks at the use of adjectives as idioms.

Some idioms are single words using parts of the body, e.g. *brainy* (intelligent), *nosy* (inquisitive) and *cheeky* (rude).

Other idioms use compound adjectives, e.g. *light-fingered* (likely to steal), *absent-minded* (forgetful) and *tight-fisted* (mean).

You can also have adjectival phrases, e.g. *full of beans* (very lively), *long in the tooth* (old) and *wet behind the ears* (young and inexperienced).

This section also examines common adjective–noun collocations, e.g. a *quick temper* (easily angered), a *narrow escape* (only just avoid danger) and more idiomatic adjective–noun combinations, e.g. a *big shot* (a very important person), a *dead heat* (a draw in a race) and a *fat chance* (no chance at all).

There is also a test on adjective–adjective combinations, e.g. *spick and span* (neat and tidy) and the section ends with idioms using specific adjectives – *good*, *bad*, *big*, *dead*, *hard*, *high*, *hot*, *long*, *short* and *thin*.

Some examples are:

put in a good word for someone (say something good about someone, especially when they are looking for a job)

flog a dead horse (waste your time doing something)

get into hot water (get into trouble)

'Stop being so self-conscious love.
Lots of men are are a bit thin on top.'

1 Describing people 1

Match the idioms on the left with the correct definitions on the right.

1	absent-minded	a	insincere, deceitful (e.g. agree when talking to someone but disagree behind their back)
2	big-headed	b	clever, intelligent
3	brainy	c	insensitive to criticism; not easily offended
4	cheeky	d	stupid, unintelligent
5	hot-headed	e	very forgetful; easily forgetting things
6	nosy	f	mean (with money)
7	pig-headed	g	rude, disrespectful (especially towards someone older, e.g. parents, teachers)
8	thick	h	stubborn; unwilling to listen to advice
9	thick-skinned	i	rich, wealthy
10	tight-fisted	j	get angry quickly; tending to do things without thinking
11	two-faced	k	conceited, boastful, self-important
12	well off	l	inquisitive, curious about others

Write your answers here:

1	2	3	4	5	6	7	8	9	10	11	12
e											

Most double adjectives are joined by a hyphen. Notice how parts of the body are often used in idioms to describe people – *cheek, head, mind, nose, skin, face* and *fist*.

2 Describing people 2

Match the idioms on the left with the correct definitions on the right.

1	down-at-heel	a	very thin
2	full of beans	b	dishonest; likely to steal things
3	heartless	c	dirty, poor, shabby, not well looked after
4	hen-pecked	d	old
5	hot-blooded	e	young and inexperienced
6	laid back	f	proud, conceited, thinking you are better than others
7	light-fingered	g	very emotional; passionate
8	long in the tooth	h	slightly bald
9	skinny	i	(of a man) always being told what to do by his wife and afraid to disagree with her
10	stuck up	j	very relaxed; not seeming to be worried about anything
11	(a bit) thin on top	k	cold and cruel
12	wet behind the ears	l	very lively

Write your answers here:

1	2	3	4	5	6	7	8	9	10	11	12
c											

It is possible to tell the age of a horse by looking at its teeth. Also, the older the horse gets, the more its gums will recede and the longer its teeth will appear to be (*long in the tooth*).

3 Describing moods, states and feelings

Fill in the missing idioms in the sentences below. To help you there is an explanation of the missing idioms after each sentence. Choose from the following:

bedridden	broke	broken-hearted	dead beat
~~down in the dumps~~	hard of hearing	ill at ease	keyed up
laid up	off-colour	on the dole	peckish
	scared stiff	tongue-tied	

1   She was really *down in the dumps* when she didn't get that job at the BBC. She'd really set her heart on it. (*depressed, unhappy*)

2   He was very shy and always felt _____ when meeting new people. (*awkward and uneasy*)

3   My uncle has been _____ for nearly a year. To be honest, I don't think he'll ever work again. (*unemployed, out of work*)

4   My aunt has been _____ for years. (*too weak to leave her bed*)

5   Although he was a great actor, he sometimes got very _____ when speaking to his fans. (*found it hard to speak easily*)

6   You haven't got anything to eat, have you, Sue? I'm feeling a bit _____ ! (*hungry*)

7   Speak up! I'm a bit _____ ! (*deaf*)

8   I'm _____ at the moment, Kevin. You couldn't lend me £20 until the weekend, could you? (*without money*)

9   Are you all right, James? You look a bit _____ .
    (*unwell, ill*)

10 My sister was _____ when her boyfriend finished
    with her. (*very sad*)

11 He was _____ for a month after his car accident. (*in
    bed*)

12 After spending the whole day walking around the shops in
    London, we were _____ . (*exhausted*)

13 I always get a bit _____ before making a speech in
    public. (*worried and nervous*)

14 I'm _____ of flying – especially taking-off and
    landing. (*terrified, really frightened*)

Although both *down in the dumps* and *broken-hearted* mean the person is
very sad and depressed, *broken-hearted* usually means you are very sad
because someone you love has died or left you.
Both *bedridden* and *laid up* mean you are in bed through illness, etc. but
bedridden is more permanent and is often associated with someone being
chronically ill or very old.

4 Describing things

A Complete the definitions below with a suitable idiom. Choose from the following:

> dog-eared   eye-catching   ~~few and far between~~
> fishy   frosty   hair-raising   long-winded
> second-hand   whole-hearted

1. If your visits to the cinema are very __*few and far between*__ , this means you don't go there very often – your visits are very infrequent.

2. If something is a bit _____ , then there is something not quite right about it. (You suspect that something is wrong.)

3. If something is _____ , it is very frightening.

4. If you give someone your _____ support, this means you support them totally.

5. A _____ welcome is a very unfriendly one.

6. If a speech is _____ , it is usually boring and goes on for too long.

7. If you buy something _____ (e.g. a car), this means that it is not new. (Someone has owned it before.)

8. If a book is _____ , the corners of the pages have been folded down, usually because it has been read a lot.

9. An _____ design is one that grabs your attention because it is attractive, unusual, etc.

B   Now complete the following sentences using five of the idioms already listed.

1   His lecture was very _____ and at least half the students walked out before the end of it.

2   The prime minister got a very _____ welcome when he visited a hospital in Liverpool two days after announcing health spending cuts.

3   You can tell lots of people have read this Harry Potter book. It's really _____ .

4   Since my parents moved to Wales, my visits to them have been very _____ .

5   There's something very _____ about this free offer. It's just too good to be true!

It certainly was a hair-raising experience!

When you are frightened, your hair sometimes stands on end, thus (*hair-raising*).

When you fold the corner of a page in a book, it resembles a dog's ear, (*dog-eared*).

Frost is very cold, so a *frosty* welcome would be a cold one.

5 Adjective + noun combinations 1

Choose the adjective (a, b, or c) which best completes each sentence.

1 I really must go and lie down for a while. I've got a ___*splitting*___ headache!

   a) cutting   b) splitting   c) ringing

2 No wonder your car won't start! Your battery's _____ .

   a) jammed   b) empty   c) flat

3 My uncle's always had a _____ spot for children. He really likes them.

   a) soft   b) kind   c) warm

4 I had a _____ escape this morning when a car almost hit me as I was cycling to work.

   a) near   b) narrow   c) close

5 It's a bit of a _____ statement to say that 'all Welsh people can sing' or 'all black people can dance'. I know lots who can't do either.

   a) sweeping   b) general   c) broad

6 I didn't like smoked salmon at first. For me it was an _____ taste. Now I really love it.

   a) experienced   b) original   c) acquired

7 I don't think Simon will ever get married. He told me he's a _____ bachelor.

   a) decided   b) confirmed   c) complete

8 One of his _____ hates was people pushing in front of him at bus stops.

   a) main   b) favourite   c) pet

9 She had a very _____ tongue, and could be really sarcastic when she was angry.

   a) bitter   b) sharp   c) cutting

10 It was the first _____ meal the tramp had had for several days.

a) compact   b) round   c) square

11 My son's always getting into trouble for fighting at school. I think that's because he has such a _____ temper.

a) loud   b) quick   c) high

12 There's an _____ law in this club that you never borrow money from a fellow member.

a) unspoken   b) understood   c) unwritten

13 'What does *inevitable* mean?'

'I haven't the _____ idea. Ask the teacher.'

a) foggiest   b) briefest   c) smallest

14 The result of the election was a(n) _____ conclusion. Everyone knew which party would win.

a) obvious   b) ready   c) foregone

15 'I don't really want to be twenty-five again,' she said to her husband. 'It was just _____ thinking!'

a) hopeful   b) wishful   c) playful

Two other idioms that mean the same as *a narrow escape* are *a close shave* and *a near miss*.

A *hot-blooded* person often has a *quick temper*.

As well as the *foggiest idea*, you can also say *faintest idea* or *slightest idea*.

6 Adjective + noun combinations 2

A Match the people on the left with the correct definitions on the right.

1	a backseat driver	**a**	someone who stops being your friend when you are having problems or difficulties
2	a big shot	**b**	a person who is being watched by someone who wants to harm or kill them
3	a blue-eyed boy	**c**	a dull or boring person who tries to spoil other people's fun
4	a dark horse	**d**	a passenger in the back of a car who gives the driver unwanted advice on how to drive
5	a fair-weather friend	**e**	a person who has greater capabilities than he/she shows or that people are aware of
6	a general dogsbody	**f**	an experienced person; someone who has done a job for a long time and is very good at it
7	a live wire	**g**	someone who has to do all the jobs no one wants to do
8	an old hand	**h**	a person who annoys everyone by claiming to know everything and trying to sound clever
9	a marked man	**i**	an important and influential person
10	a rough diamond	**j**	a very active and lively person
11	a smart aleck	**k**	a man who is liked and admired by someone in authority (e.g. his boss)
12	a wet blanket	**l**	someone who looks rather rude, rough and unfriendly but who is actually kind and generous

Write your answers here:

1	2	3	4	5	6	7	8	9	10	11	12
d											

B Look at the four drawings. Which idioms do they remind you of? Choose from those already listed.

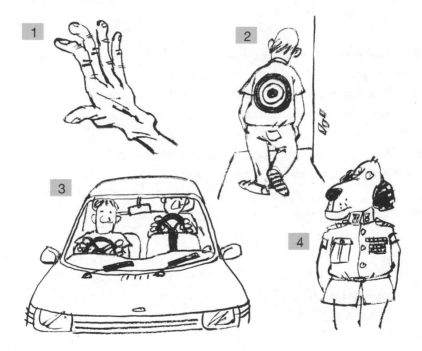

 Another word for a *big shot* is a *bigwig*.

The phrase *a dark horse* comes from horse racing. A dark horse was a fairly unknown horse whose abilities were kept secret until it came to the race track and, hopefully, won the race.

A live wire is a reference to a wire which has a 'live' electric current running through it.

In the idiom *a marked man*, the word 'marked' here really means 'watched'.

7 Adjective + noun combinations 3

Say whether the idioms in the following sentences are used correctly (true) or incorrectly (false).

		True	False
1	We were late, so we took a **short cut** through the park.	✓	_____
2	A woman would probably be pleased if a man gave her a **dirty look**, and vice-versa.	_____	_____
3	**Hobson's choice** is no real choice at all.	_____	_____
4	The two runners finished the race at the same time. It was a **dead heat**.	_____	_____
5	Most people would be too embarrassed to tell others that they had a **plum job**.	_____	_____
6	I hate **tight spots**, so I never get into lifts. I always use the stairs instead.	_____	_____
7	In Britain, when a couple have been married for fifty years, they are often given a **golden handshake**.	_____	_____
8	To get a job you need a permanent address, but to be able to rent a flat you need to have a job. It's a **vicious circle**.	_____	_____
9	Don't believe a word he says; it's just another of his **tall stories**.	_____	_____

		True	False
10	Daniel is Catholic and his wife is Methodist so they went to the local church for a **mixed blessing**.	_____	_____
11	He can speak two languages fluently – he's **double Dutch**.	_____	_____
12	If something was a **long shot**, it might not have a great chance of succeeding.	_____	_____
13	A **flying visit** is a very short trip in an aeroplane.	_____	_____
14	Don't mention last year's Christmas party to Harry. It's a bit of a **sore point** with him. That's when he split up with his girlfriend.	_____	_____
15	I felt really pleased when she told me that she thought I had a **fat chance** of getting the job.	_____	_____

The expression *Hobson's choice* refers to Tobias Hobson who lived in Cambridge during the sixteenth century. He owned a stable and used to hire out horses. However, he only allowed his customers to choose the horse nearest the stable door – the one that had run the least recently. So, in effect, the customers couldn't choose their horse at all.

8 Adjective pairs

Complete the paired idioms in the sentences below. Choose from the following adjectives:

> alive   dried   dry   early   easy   fast   less   low   sound   spick
> square   surely   sweet   thin   tired   void   white   ~~worse~~

1   For *better or* _____**worse**_____ , the mobile phone is now a normal part of people's lives.

2   He drove *slowly but* _____ .

3   She was beaten *fair and* _____ by her opponent in the first round at Wimbledon.

4   'How's your father these days?'
    'Still _____ *and kicking*. He's living in Brighton now.'

5   Oh, thank goodness you're both *safe and* _____ . I was so worried about you!

6   They promised to stand by each other *through thick and*
    _____ .

7   He won't believe anything unless he actually sees it *in black and*
    _____ .

8   If we win next Saturday, we'll be *home and* _____ for a place in the next round of the Cup.

9   John's a farmer and has to get up *bright and* _____
    every morning.

10   The contract was declared *null and* _____ , as one of the partners had forgotten to sign it.

11   Could you wait – I'm *more or* _____ ready now.

12   He lived a very *free and* _____ life in the country.

13   Natalia is *sick and* _____ of hearing about how 'wonderful' and 'clever' her neighbour's children are!

14   The police have searched *high and* _____ for the missing teenager, Connie Brown. But they still haven't found any trace of her.

15   I'm afraid you'll have to wear a jacket, sir. It's a *hard and* _____ rule at the club.

16   The lecture was just how the students liked it – *short and* _____ .

17   The result of tomorrow's match is *cut and* _____ , New Zealand is bound to win.

18   Her flat was so _____ *and span* that it looked more like a well-kept museum than a home.

 The word *span* comes from a very old Norse word that means a chip of wood which has been freshly cut.

9 Idioms using common adjectives

Complete sentences 1–15 by choosing an ending from a–o.

1   Sally's not speaking to me. I ...

2   If you're applying for a job with my company, I'll ...

3   Since Tom Blake got that book of poems published, he's ...

4   Have I upset Emma in some way? I said hello to her and she just ...

5   It's like *flogging a dead horse* trying to teach Richard to ...

6   Last year the Patel family decided to leave Britain *for good* and ...

7   I'm a bit *hard up* at the moment, so I ...

8   Of course Olaf likes you. He's just ...

9   You'll be for the *high jump* when dad ...

10   You're nearly thirty now. Isn't it *high time* you ...

11   The politician got very *hot under the collar* when the journalist ...

12   Your son is very talented, Mrs Cappelli and ...

13   He *got into hot water* for ...

14   We had to *cut* our holiday *short* when my wife ...

15   Taxis in this town after midnight ...

a	finds out you've been smoking. You know how much he hates it!
b	use a computer. I don't think he'll ever learn!
c	using the office phone for private calls.
d	accused him of taking bribes.
e	try and *put in a good word* for you.
f	seem to be pretty *thin on the ground*.
g	*cut me dead*.
h	should *go a long way*.
i	*playing hard to get*, that's all!
j	must be *in her bad books*.
k	broke her leg on our first day on the ski slope.
l	settle in New Zealand.
m	become *too big for his boots*.
n	stopped living with your parents and got a flat of your own?
o	can't afford to go out with you tonight.

Write your answers here:

1	2	3	4	5	6	7	8	9	10	11	12	13	14	15
j														

The opposite of being in someone's *bad books* is to be in someone's *good books*.

To *flog* is to beat a person or animal with a whip or stick. If the animal is already dead, then it's rather pointless!

10 Just for fun 1

Complete the crossword. All the idioms are found in Tests 1–9.

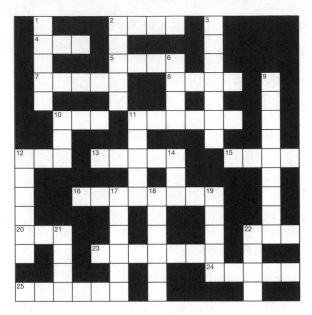

Across

2   There is a hard and _____ rule here that visitors are not allowed in guests' rooms after 11 o'clock at night.

4   We really got into _____ water when we borrowed the school DVD player without asking.

5   My uncle has always had a _____ spot for Ireland, so I'm not surprised he's decided to move there.

7   Johann's a bit of a _____ diamond, but he's got a heart of gold!

8   Horror novels are really _____ -raising.

10   Wearing a suit and tie was one of his _____ hates.

11   Some people get very _____ -tied when talking in front of large groups of people.

12   I hate Françoise's new boyfriend. He's so _____ -headed!

13   She told me she'd seen my ex-wife last week and that she was still _____ and kicking.

15   'Are you and Matt getting married then?'
'Don't be so _____ ! It's none of your business!'

16   I hate driving with my brother-in-law in the back. He's a real _____ driver and is always criticizing the way I drive.

20   Poor David! He's really _____ -pecked and won't do a thing
      without asking his wife first.

22   He's still a bit _____ behind the ears. But he'll soon learn.

23   Come on, enjoy the party! Don't be such a wet _____ .

24   You're flogging a dead _____ trying to teach Marco to dance.
      He's got two left feet!

25   You look a bit off-_____ , Aaron. Aren't you feeling well?

Down

1   The teacher had a very _____ tongue, and most of the pupils
      were frightened of her and what she might say to them.

2   There's something _____ about his business. I'm sure he's up to
      no good.

3   My cousin eats when he's depressed. Then he puts on weight
      which makes him even more depressed, so he eats again. It's a
      _____ circle!

6   I hate to say this, darling, but you're starting to get a bit _____
      on top.

9   He left the company with a golden _____ of nearly $90,000.

10   Chandler's so _____-headed, isn't he? I don't think I've met
      anyone quite as stubborn as him.

11   To be a politician, you have to be very _____-skinned.

12   We decided to leave Lisbon _____ and early and to head for the
      south coast.

14   It was a very _____-catching design.

17   He got very hot under the _____ when I accused him of lying.

18   You need to eat some more, Bethany! You're far too _____ !

19   Don't you think you're a bit long in the _____ to be partying
      all night?

21   If a person remarries, then any old will they have made is
      declared _____ and void.

22   I'm looking for a job. Could you put in a good _____ for me
      with your boss?

Section 2:
Idioms using nouns

This section looks at the use of nouns as idioms.

It starts with common nouns to describe people – either single nouns or compound nouns. These can be positive, e.g. a *whizz kid* (someone with lots of modern ideas, energy and enthusiasm and who achieves a lot while still young) or negative, e.g. a *busybody* (someone who always wants to know about other people's private lives).

There are idioms based on phrasal verbs, e.g. a *break-in* (burglary) and a *tailback* (long line of traffic), as well as fairly abstract single noun idioms, e.g. an *eyesore* (something ugly to look at) and a *snag* (a hidden problem or difficulty).

Compound nouns are also examined, e.g. a *busman's holiday* (a holiday spent doing the same work as you would do in your job) and a *stag party* (an all-male party for someone getting married).

There are also idioms based on noun phrases, e.g. a *bolt from the blue* (a sudden and unexpected event) and a *flash in the pan* (something that is suddenly popular but only lasts for a short while).

This section ends by looking at pairs of nouns, e.g. *flesh and blood* (members of your own family) plus specific nouns used in idiomatic phrases – *end, mind, point, line, word, way* and *time*.

Some examples are:

be at a loose end (not have anything to do)

drop someone a line (write a letter to someone)

slip one's mind (forget)

'I hear there's a 200-metre tailback!'

11 Types of people 1

SECTION 2

Match the idioms on the left with the correct definitions on the right.

1	the apple of someone's eye	a	someone who spends a lot of time sitting and watching television
2	a bighead	b	someone who turns up at parties without being invited to them
3	a blackleg	c	the minimum number of people that can run an office successfully
4	a busybody	d	a person who loves taking dangerous risks
5	a chatterbox	e	the person someone loves most and is very proud of (e.g. a grandchild)
6	a couch potato	f	someone with lots of modern ideas, energy and enthusiasm and who achieves a lot while still young
7	a daredevil	g	a person who talks a lot especially about things that are unimportant
8	a figurehead	h	someone who continues to work when their fellow workers are on strike
9	a gatecrasher	i	someone who is the leader of a country or organization, but in name only. He or she doesn't have any real power
10	a pain in the neck	j	someone who always wants to know about other people's private lives
11	a skeleton staff	k	someone who is very conceited, vain or boastful
12	a whizz kid	l	a person who is very annoying

Write your answers here:

1	2	3	4	5	6	7	8	9	10	11	12
e											

Bighead comes from the adjective *big-headed*.
To *chatter* means to talk quickly without stopping. A *chat* is an informal, friendly conversation.
A *couch* is another word for sofa.

12 Types of people 2

Look at the drawings below. Find the following people:

an early bird	_2_	a guinea pig	___	a jailbird	___
a killjoy	___	a night owl	___	a nosy parker	___
a road hog	___	a rolling stone	___	a scapegoat	___
a skinflint	___	a troublemaker	___	a white-collar worker	___

To *hog* means to keep or use all of something. If you *hog the road* you drive so badly that you take up too much space.

Joy is another word for 'fun' or 'happiness'. So if you kill someone's joy then you're stopping them being happy.

Office workers in the UK traditionally wear a suit and a white shirt. People who do hard physical work where they often get dirty are called *blue-collar workers*.

A *rolling stone* comes from the proverb *a rolling stone gathers no moss*.

13 Nouns from phrasal verbs

Complete the newspaper headlines below with a suitable idiom. Choose from the following and write the correct letter (a–o) in the gaps.

a	BREAKDOWN	f	HOLD-UP	k	OUTLOOK
b	BREAK-IN	g	KICK-OFF	l	SETBACK
c	COMEBACK	h	KNOCKOUT	m	TAILBACK
d	CUTBACKS	i	MIX-UP	n	TURNOVER
e	DOWNPOUR	j	OUTBREAK	o	WRITE-UP

1

> **THIRD _b_ IN PEACEFUL SURREY VILLAGE THIS MONTH**
> (burglary)

2

> **2-MILE _____ ON M1 AFTER MOTORWAY ACCIDENT**
> (traffic that is moving slowly or not moving at all)

3

> **SUDDEN _____ OF LEAD SINGER CAUSES BAND TO CANCEL BRITISH TOUR**
> (medical condition where you are mentally ill and unable to cope with life)

4

> **NEW LLOYD-WEBBER MUSICAL GETS GOOD _____ IN LONDON EVENING STANDARD**
> (review)

5

> **HEAVY _____ RUINS FREE OPEN-AIR CONCERT IN HYDE PARK**
> (rainfall)

6

> **WEATHER _____ FOR SUMMER IS NOT VERY PROMISING**
> (forecast)

7 FAMOUS 80s BAND TO MAKE A _____
(an attempt to become popular again)

8 ROBBERS GET AWAY WITH £800,000 IN
DARING _____ IN BROAD DAYLIGHT
(robbery)

9 HEAVYWEIGHT CHAMPION LOSES BY A _____
IN THE FIRST ROUND
(by being hit so hard that you become unconscious)

10 HOSPITAL RECORDS _____ CAUSES CHAOS
(mistake that causes problems)

11 NEW GENERATION OF MOBILE PHONES
INCREASES FIRM'S _____ BY 200%
(total income from sales)

12 FA CUP _____ DELAYED FOR 20 MINUTES
DUE TO DEMONSTRATION BY REFEREES
(start of football match)

13 GOVERNMENT THREATENS _____ TO THE
HEALTH SERVICE
(reduced funding)

14 DOCTORS FEAR _____ OF CHOLERA
AFTER EARTHQUAKE IN TURKEY
(a cholera epidemic)

15 TUNNEL PROJECT BETWEEN WALES AND IRELAND
SUFFERS SERIOUS _____
(delay in its progress)

You can also have an *outbreak* of war, fighting or spots.
You can also have a *breakdown* in your car – when your car stops because
there is something wrong with it.

14 Single nouns

A Match the idioms on the left with the correct definitions on the right.

1	a blackout	a	something very unpleasant to look at (e.g. a building)	
2	a best-seller	b	a loud whistle or cry of disapproval (e.g. from an audience at a theatre or a crowd at a football match)	
3	a bottleneck	c	(of a country, organization) the time when they were most powerful, successful or popular	
4	a brainwave	d	a situation or event from which you learn something surprising or something that you did not know before	
5	a catcall	e	a sum of money that you get unexpectedly, such as winning the football pools or a lottery, etc.	
6	a catnap	f	extra advantages on top of your regular salary (e.g. a company car, lunch vouchers)	
7	an eye-opener	g	a book that sells in very large numbers; a successful book	
8	an eyesore	h	a short sleep in a chair (not in a bed)	
9	a gimmick	i	a small mistake in a law that makes it possible to avoid doing something that the law is supposed to make you do (e.g. a tax loophole)	
10	a heyday	j	an electricity failure (when everything goes black)	
11	a loophole	k	where the road narrows so that a traffic jam is quickly formed	
12	a perk	l	a difficulty or problem – often hidden or unexpected	

| 13 | a snag | m | some sort of trick, device or unusual action whose purpose is to attract attention or publicity, usually when trying to sell something to people |

| 14 | a windfall | n | a sudden clever thought or idea |

Write your answers here:

1	2	3	4	5	6	7	8	9	10	11	12	13	14
j													

B Look at the four drawings. Which idioms would you use to complete them? Choose from those already listed.

When you are surprised your eyes often open wide (*eye-opener*) and something that is not very nice to look at can make your eyes very sore (an *eyesore*).
A *nap* is a short sleep. Cats can sleep anywhere at any time (*catnap*).
To remember *blackout*, imagine that the lights go *out*, so everything is very *black*.

15 Noun phrases 1

What do the following idioms mean? Choose the best alternative (a, b or c).

1 Our hotel was only a **stone's throw** from the beach.

a) It was on the beach.

b) It was a long way from the beach.

c) It was close to the beach.

2 Have you been invited to Basil's **stag party**?

a) an all-male party for someone getting married

b) an eighteenth birthday party

c) a party on someone's last day at work

3 I'm having a **busman's holiday** this summer teaching English to a group of French students.

a) a short holiday abroad

b) a holiday spent doing the same work as you do in your job

c) a holiday which also involves a lot of travelling

4 To most people, a Rolls-Royce is still something of a **status symbol**.

a) an unnecessary luxury

b) a possession they hope to have one day

c) a possession that shows others that you have money or position

5 It was a **dead-end job** and she hated it.

a) a very boring job

b) a job without prospects

c) a physically hard and dirty job

6 It's typical of him to take all the credit when we're the ones who've done all the **donkey work**.

a) all the work at the start of the project

b) all the work without getting paid for it

c) all the real hard work

7 They phoned me up today and told me I've been put on the **shortlist**.

a) the list of people waiting to go into hospital for an operation
b) the list of the most suitable people for a job
c) the list of people waiting for government housing

8 You won't get your shoes clean like that. Use some **elbow grease**!

a) put more effort into polishing your shoes
b) use a special type of shoe polish
c) use a very hard brush to polish your shoes

9 We were late for work because we got stuck in a **traffic jam**.

a) We were involved in a car accident.
b) We got stuck in heavy snow.
c) We were in a long line of cars which were moving very slowly.

10 The bar they worked at in Spain paid them **chicken feed**.

a) a small wage plus all they could eat
b) gave them cash at the end of each day
c) hardly any money at all

11 Everyone should have a **nest egg**. You never know when you might need it.

a) a life insurance policy
b) an amount of money saved for future use
c) a special place you can go to when you want to be alone

12 Roberto wasn't very happy at work, but the **last straw** came when a much younger man was given promotion.

a) he received the final insult
b) the last in a series of unpleasant things that have happened to him at work
c) he suffered a nervous breakdown

13 She had lots of **teething problems** in her new job, but things seem all right now.

a) early difficulties
b) problems of water seeping in
c) staff problems

14 If you want my opinion, learning to use the Internet is **child's play**.

a) lots of fun
b) very easy to do
c) only for young people

15 There was a big headline in today's paper: Minister admits paying **hush money** to French model.

a) government money which the public know nothing about
b) money from drugs
c) money to keep something secret

Hush is a word you use when you want someone to be silent.

An all-female party for a woman about to get married is called a *hen party* (or a *shower* in American English).

Jam is very sticky, so we usually say *get stuck in a traffic jam*.

Nest egg originated in the seventeenth century and was an egg made of china that a farmer put in a hen's nest to encourage it to lay more eggs.

If a baby is *teething*, its first teeth are growing and it is often uncomfortable or unwell.

16 Noun phrases 2

Choose the word (a, b or c) which best completes each sentence. To help you, the meaning of the idiom is given in brackets after each sentence.

1   'What was the exam like, Carol?'
    'Great! It was a piece of _____ *cake* _____ .'

    a) cheese   (b) cake   c) old rope
    (Meaning: *It was very easy.*)

2   The resignation of the chairman of the board came like a bolt
    from _____ .

    a) the sky   b) above   c) the blue
    (Meaning: *It was sudden and unexpected.*)

3   The so-called scandal turned out to be nothing more than a storm
    in _____ .

    a) an ocean   b) a teacup   c) a bucket
    (Meaning: *A lot of fuss and excitement about something that is not
    really important.*)

4   To be a politician it helps if you have the gift of the
    _____ .

    a) gab   b) lip   c) tongue
    (Meaning: *You are able to speak fluently, confidently and
    persuasively.*)

5   He was £100,000 in debt. His friend offered to lend him £500, but
    it was just a drop in the _____ to what he really needed.

    a) swimming pool   b) lake   c) ocean
    (Meaning: *A very small amount compared with what is actually needed.*)

6   Today's revelation in the newspaper about police corruption is
    just the tip of the _____ . If you ask me, there's a lot
    more to come.

    a) mountain   b) needle   c) iceberg
    (Meaning: *Only the start of something that is much bigger, most of
    which is still waiting to be discovered or revealed.*)

7 'Which is the _____ one out in these three words: sparrow, eagle, snake?'
'Snake! The other two are birds.'

a) strange   b) odd   c) next
(Meaning: *Which word is different from the rest.*)

8 I'd hate to be the politician who said publicly that in his opinion 'the Internet was just a flash in the _____ .'

a) pan   b) fire   c) mirror
(Meaning: *It would be suddenly popular but would only last a short time.*)

9 If you're going to run for mayor, just make sure there are no _____ in the cupboard! You know what the press are like.

a) moths   b) skeletons   c) ghosts
(Meaning: *Make sure you don't have anything in your past that could be embarrassing or shameful.*)

10 He had been a market trader for years and offered to show his nephew the tricks of the _____ .

a) job   b) trade   c) profession
(Meaning: *The best ways and clever methods of being successful.*)

11 My answer to the quiz question 'Who composed the Midnight Sonata?' was just a shot in the _____ . I didn't really know it was Beethoven.

a) night   b) air   c) dark
(Meaning: *A wild guess.*)

12 I didn't really mean to say that – it was just a slip of the _____ .

a) mouth   b) jaw   c) tongue
(Meaning: *You said something you didn't really mean to say.*)

13 It was an excellent dinner party. The only _____ in the ointment was Helen spilling red wine over our new carpet.

a) finger   b) fly   c) stone
(Meaning: *A small problem or minor incident that spoils something that is otherwise perfect.*)

14 Not getting that teaching job in Florida was _____ in disguise. The school was destroyed by a hurricane the very same week I was due to start.

a) luck   b) the devil   c) a blessing
(Meaning: *Something which appears bad at first but then turns out well.*)

15 Well, well, if it isn't Celia Durban! You're a sight for _____ eyes!

a) old   b) blue   c) sore
(Meaning: *You are really pleased to see someone. A very welcome sight.*)

A *bolt from the blue* refers to a sudden thunderbolt from a blue sky.
A *drop in the ocean* is known as *a drop in the bucket* in American English.
Since an ocean is very large, anything dropped into it would hardly be noticed.
Only one-ninth of an iceberg is visible. The rest is hidden beneath the sea – so there is still a great deal to be revealed (*tip of the iceberg*).
If you *shoot* at something in the *dark*, you are very unlikely to hit the target. So it's a very wild shot!

17 Noun pairs

Fill in the missing pairs of nouns in the sentences below. Choose from the following:

back to front	cock and bull	~~fingers and thumbs~~
flesh and blood	fun and games	hand in glove
head and shoulders	hustle and bustle	life and soul
nook and cranny	pros and cons	skin and bone
tooth and nail	ups and downs	wear and tear

1 Don't let Ross do the washing-up. He's bound to drop something. He's all _fingers and thumbs_ .

2 We looked in every _____ for the missing ring, but couldn't find it anywhere.

3 Paul was so funny on Saturday. He was the _____ of the party!

4 This carpet is made from a brand-new type of fibre and should stand up to a lot of _____ .

5 I like living in a small village in Wales, but there are times when I miss the _____ of London.

6 You're not eating enough! Just look at you! You're all _____ !

7 He gave us some _____ story about being abducted by aliens to explain why he was late for work.

8 The police are working _____ with the Football Association in an effort to stamp out soccer violence.

9   You can't throw her out, surely? Not your sister – not your own
_____ !

10   He couldn't understand why the students were laughing until he
noticed that he'd got his jumper on _____ .

11   The managing director carefully outlined the
_____ of the proposed merger.

12   As soon as the teacher went out of the classroom, the children got
up to all sorts of _____ .

13   Louis and Anne-Marie are always fighting
_____ . I'm surprised they haven't got
divorced yet.

14   Kimberley was an outstanding student who was
_____ above the others in the class.

15   Life is full of _____ , isn't it? You just hope you
get more happy moments than sad ones.

Nook is an old word for *corner* and *cranny* is an old word for crack.
Hustle means 'busy and noisy activity'.
The verb *bustle* means to move around quickly looking very busy.

18 Idioms using common nouns 1

Read the speech bubbles below and then decide which idioms are being described. Choose from the following:

END

be at the end of your tether   _4_

be at a loose end   _____

get hold of the wrong end
of the stick   _____

It's not the end of the world!   _____

make ends meet   _____

LINE

drop someone a line   _____

read between the lines   _____

toe the line   _____

MIND

a weight off your mind   _____

can't make up your mind   _____

give someone a piece
of your mind   _____

slip your mind   _____

POINT

at point-blank range   _____

I take your point!   _____

What's the point?   _____

1 I know she says she's happy in her letter, but I've just got this feeling she's hiding something.

2 He was annoying me so much that I told him what I thought of him!

3 Write to me some time!

4 I've tried everything to stop the baby crying. I just don't know what to do next.

5

The snake was less than a foot away from her when she shot it. She couldn't miss!

6

Of course I'll do as I'm told.

7

You've misunderstood us completely. That's not what we meant at all!

8

What good is it complaining to the travel company. They won't do anything about it!

9

Shall I take the tabby or the ginger one? Oh it's so hard to choose, they're both so cute!

10

I spend more than I earn. What am I going to do? It's so hard to manage.

11

Yes, I understand what you're saying – you are quite right.

12

I've just seen the doctor again and he said there is no need for an operation after all. What a relief!

13

For the first time in my life I'm out of work! What am I going to do?

14

Oh I'm sorry about the lottery ticket, Helga. I forgot all about it!

15

I don't have anything to do this week.

If an animal is tied to a *tether* (a rope attached to a post), it can only get a certain distance – no more.

You can also refuse to do something *point blank*, (I told him *point blank* I wouldn't do it!) which means you do so directly and without trying to explain your reasons.

In *I take your point*, 'point' here is short for 'point of view' or opinion.

Section 2: Idioms using nouns **37**

19 Idioms using common nouns 2

Say whether the idioms in the following sentences are used correctly (true) or incorrectly (false).

		True	False
1	I promised him. **I gave him my word.**	✓	
2	We'll have to ask someone for directions. **I just don't know which way to turn.**		
3	If you are **having a whale of a time,** you are probably not enjoying yourself.		
4	She was offended. She **took it the wrong way.**		
5	He's in prison. He's **doing time.**		
6	Justin is very hard to understand because he doesn't **mince his words.**		
7	If you are really angry with someone, you might **have words** with them.		
8	We checked the weather forecast to see **which way the wind was blowing.**		
9	The parcel was delayed – it arrived **in next to no time.**		
10	He's going to be a famous actor one day. **You mark my words!**		
11	Most soldiers are able to march **in good time.**		
12	Charles and I **go back a long way.** In fact, we started school at the same time.		
13	His house is a bit **out of the way.** In other words it's very modern.		

14   'Mum's the word!' Remember – it's a secret!   _____   _____

15   The fire brigade arrived **in the nick of time**.
Two minutes later and the house would
have burnt down.   _____   _____

16   Mr Leung translated what the Chinese
prime minister said. He took **the words
out of his mouth**.   _____   _____

17   Watching TV or reading a book are two
good ways of **killing time**.   _____   _____

Having a whale of time!

To *serve time* can also mean when you are in prison.

A *nick* is a tiny cut (or notch) in a piece of wood. Long ago people would
keep the score when playing a game by cutting notches in a piece of wood.
If one team scored at the last minute and won the match, then that nick
was known as the *nick in time*.

20 Just for fun 2

Complete the word puzzle to find the well-known proverb. All the idioms are found in Tests 11–19.

#												
1	B	L	A	C	K	L	E	G				
2									Y			
3			O						K			
4			R		N							
5									R			
6				H								
7									D			
8				D				P				
9					O							
10					D							
11									K			
12								R				
13								T				
14				S				F				
15								L				
16					C				G			
17								O				
18								K				
19				N								
20		B								K		

1   I could never be a _____ . I would never go on working
    if my fellow workmates were on strike.

2   He was an _____ bird and usually got up at six o'clock in
    the morning.

3   News is just coming in of a serious _____ of cholera in
    Taiwan.

4   A _____ is a sudden clever idea.

5   Don't take any notice. It's just a _____ in a teacup. It'll
    soon be forgotten.

6   Perhaps we shouldn't let Alex carry that vase! He's all fingers and
    _____ !

7   This exam is easy. It's _____ 's play!

8   Halfway through the football match there was a sudden
    _____ and the players got soaked.

9   Lesley is going to be a top opera singer one day. You mark my
    _____ !

10 Now that I'm out of work, it's really hard to make _____
    meet.

11 No, I didn't mean that at all! You've got hold of the wrong end of
    the _____ again!

12 He lived just a stone's _____ from Lake Garda.

13 My aunt has the _____ of the gab. She'd make an
    excellent politician.

14 He hates spending money. He's a real _____ !

15 We decided to _____ time by playing a game of cards.

16 After the protest the leader of the council was made a
_____ and forced to resign.

17 If you're at a _____ end this weekend, why not come
round to see us?

18 The ambulance arrived just in the _____ of time to save
the patient's life.

19 We looked in every _____ and cranny for the lost
document, but couldn't find it anywhere.

20 Try to avoid driving along the High Street in the mornings as it's
a bit of a _____ during the rush hour.

The missing proverb is:

_____

(*You use this to say jokingly that you and someone else must be very
intelligent because you both agree about something.*)

Section 3: Idioms using verbs

This section concentrates on the use of verbs as idioms.

Certain verbs are nearly always followed by certain nouns. This section starts by looking at some common verb–noun collocations where the same verb is used for several nouns, e.g. *break* (your leg, the ice), *catch* (a cold, fire) and *lose* (your temper, face).

More idiomatic verb–noun combinations are presented next, e.g. *get the sack* (lose your job), *hit the sack* (go to bed) and *spill the beans* (reveal secret information).

The rest of the section concentrates on the most common verbs used in idioms, i.e. *give*, *take*, *break*, *have*, *make*, *bring*, *come*, *go*, *get*, *keep*, *pull*, *put* and *turn*.

Some examples are:

give someone the cold shoulder (ignore someone)

take someone for a ride (deceive someone in order to get money from them)

have a lump in one's throat (feel very emotional and close to tears)

make a mountain out of a molehill (exaggerate a situation)

keep a straight face (stop oneself from laughing)

pull someone's leg (tease someone)

'Something's put the wind up him!'

21 Verb + noun collocations

Add two more words or phrases to the verbs below. Use each word or phrase once only. Choose from the following:

> a cold   a conclusion   a living   a speech   attention
> between the lines   face   fire   ~~permission~~   someone a compliment
> someone's palm   thanks   the curtains   the fort   the ice
> the impression   the line   ~~the way~~   your leg   your temper

1	**ask**	a question	_permission_	_the way_
2	**break**	a promise		
3	**catch**	a bus		
4	**draw**	a picture		
5	**give**	advice		
6	**hold**	a meeting		
7	**lose**	weight		
8	**make**	a profit		
9	**pay**	a bill		
10	**read**	a book		

You *catch a disease* when it is infectious or contagious (e.g. the 'flu').
Companies can also *make a loss*, when they lose money instead of making it.
It is also possible to say *earn a living*.

22 Verb + noun combinations 1

Two out of the three nouns (in brackets) can go with each verb to form idioms.
Underline the noun which does **not** form an idiom.

1 break (the news, the ice, <u>the time</u>)

2 call (the shots, someone's bluff, the handle)

3 do (a speech, wonders, the trick)

4 get (the message, the bacon, the sack)

5 go (public, places, one's goat)

6 have (words, pieces, kittens)

7 hit (the boat, the sack, the jackpot)

8 jump (the gun, the traffic, the queue)

9 make (a move, a bomb, steam)

10 play (the roof, second fiddle, the fool)

11 pull (strings, the beans, one's weight)

12 run (riot, the gauntlet, reason)

13 see (the ropes, the light, the sights)

14 take (the plunge, the biscuit, the bucket)

15 throw (a party, the fence, a fit)

Short verb + noun combinations are very common in idiomatic English. It is
best to learn each one as a phrase, rather than trying to remember the verb
and noun separately.
Jump the gun is a reference to a runner starting a race before the gun goes
off.

23 Verb + noun combinations 2

Take a verb from box A and a noun from box B to complete the definitions below. Use each word once only.

A

bury	cook	drop	fly
~~go~~	kick	lose	pop
sit	smell	spill	stretch
	surf	talk	

B

beans	books	bucket
clanger	fence	~~halves~~
handle	hatchet	legs
nerve	net	question
	rat	shop

1 When you ___*go halves*___ , you divide the cost of something equally between you – that is, fifty-fifty.

2 To _____ the _____ means to dishonestly change a company's bookkeeping records in order to steal money.

3 If you _____ the _____ , you ask someone to marry you.

4 To _____ the _____ is to use a computer to visit various sites on the Internet for information that is of interest to you.

5 When you _____ the _____ , you stop quarrelling or arguing with someone and agree to be friends again.

6 To _____ _____ is to talk about your job with those you work with – usually when you are away from your place of work.

7 If you decide to _____ your _____ , this means you want to go for a walk – especially after you have been sitting down for a while.

8   When you _____ a _____ , you say something embarrassing in front of others.

9   To _____ the _____ is a slightly humorous way of saying 'to die'.

10   To _____ on the _____ is to avoid making a decision between two sides in an argument or competition.

11   If you _____ your _____ , you no longer have the courage you once had to do something (e.g. climb a mountain, make a speech in public).

12   To _____ the _____ is to tell people secret information.

13   To _____ off the _____ is to become very angry suddenly – to lose your temper.

14   To _____ a _____ is to become suspicious about a situation – to think that something wrong or dishonest is happening.

Net is short for 'Internet'.

Spill the beans refers to the Ancient Greek tradition of using beans to count votes. A jar would be passed around and voters would put a white bean for *No* and a brown bean for *Yes*. If the jar was knocked over, you could see which way the vote was going.

In Britain during the Black Death plague, people were encouraged to keep pets at home to smell out and kill rats (*smell a rat*).

24 Idioms using *give* and *take*

A   For each sentence in **I** find a suitable idiom from **II**. Write your answers in the box.

I

1. She promised me she would do it.

2. Daniel completely ignored me this morning when I said hello to him.

3. It was supposed to be a surprise party, but Sarah told Thomas about it.

4. The shopkeeper chased the two shoplifters, but they escaped.

5. The audience clapped loudly when the band appeared on stage.

6. Phöebe helped her neighbour with her son's wedding preparations.

7. Javier telephoned his girlfriend after work.

8. My brother lost his job last week. His boss told him to leave after he had refused to work overtime.

II

a. They gave them a big hand.

b. He gave him the sack.

c. They gave him the slip.

d. He gave her a bell.

e. She gave me her word.

f. She gave the game away.

g. He gave me the cold shoulder.

h. She gave her a hand.

Write your answers here:

1	2	3	4	5	6	7	8
e							

B   Replace the words in italics in the sentences below with an idiom from the box.

(not) take no for an answer   take it or leave it

take it out on someone   take place

take pot luck   take someone for a ride

take something by storm   take something with a pinch of salt

take the floor   ~~take to one's heels~~

take things easy

---

1   The two boys *ran away* when the farmer chased them.
The two boys _took to their heels_ when the farmer chased them.

2   Let's check the Internet to see if there are any last-minute, cheap holidays going somewhere tomorrow. It doesn't matter where – we'll just *take a chance*.

3   Nimah tends to exaggerate a lot. If I were you *I wouldn't believe everything he tells you*.

4   The new British boy band has *been really successful in America*.

5   I told him he couldn't borrow my new laptop, but he kept on asking anyway. *He just refused to accept my refusal.*

6   It was only when he got home after the car boot sale that he found out the TV didn't work. The woman he had bought it from had *cheated him*.

7　His doctor told him to *relax and avoid stress* for a while.

8　Just because someone has stolen your mobile phone, there's no need to *behave unpleasantly towards* me. It wasn't my fault!

9　$10,000 – and that's my final offer! *It's up to you if you accept it or not.*

10　There was an expectant hush as the guest speaker *got up to speak.*

11　They told everyone that their wedding would *be held* at St Mary's church on 18th September.

The *heel* is the bottom back part of a shoe and is what you see when someone runs away from you.
To *take pot luck* used to mean to take whatever food was served from a cooking pot.

25 Idioms using *break*, *have* and *make*

A Arrange the following under the correct verb. There should be five under each.

a bee in one's bonnet

a bone to pick with someone

a chip on one's shoulder

a good time

a lump in one's throat

a mountain out of a molehill

a scene

~~even~~

fun of someone

one's blood boil

one's word

short work of something

someone's heart

the back of something

the news

BREAK

even

_____

_____

_____

_____

HAVE

_____

_____

_____

_____

_____

MAKE

_____

_____

_____

_____

_____

B   Complete the sentences below using one of the above idioms and making any changes that may be necessary. To help you, a definition is given after each sentence.

1   I honestly don't know what all the fuss is about. If you ask me they're just _making a mountain out of a molehill_ . (*making a lot of fuss about nothing*)

2   My father refuses to use a mobile phone. He's got _____ about mobile phones causing brain tumours. (*a fixed idea; is obsessed with the idea*)

3   With any luck the company should _____ by the end of the year. (*make neither a profit nor a loss*)

4   You'd better keep away from Julian. He's got _____ with you about not turning up for the match on Saturday. (*a complaint to make*)

5   It really _____ when young people don't give up their seat on a bus for older people. (*makes me angry*)

6   Michael's on holiday somewhere in Spain, so they still haven't been able to _____ to him of his nephew's birth. (*tell him what's happened*)

7   Most British people hate _____ in public. That's why they rarely complain at restaurants. (*quarrelling; making a fuss*)

8   It _____ André's _____ when Katerina left him. (*made him really sad; really upset him*)

9   You shouldn't _____ his clothes. He likes wearing yellow! (*laugh or make jokes about*)

10   Lucinda has always _____ about not going to university. (*felt resentful, inferior*)

If you get angry, your blood pressure normally rises, so if you were really angry it might feel as if your blood was boiling!

26 Idioms using *bring*, *come* and *go*

Complete the newspaper headlines below with a suitable idiom. Write the correct letter (a–n) in the gaps. Choose from the following:

a	BRINGS THE HOUSE DOWN	h	COME TO LIGHT
b	BROUGHT TO LIGHT	i	COME TO NOTHING
c	COMES A CROPPER	j	GOES BALLISTIC
d	COMES CLEAN	k	GOES BUST
e	CAME DOWN IN THE WORLD	l	GO DUTCH
f	COMES INTO FORCE	m	GOES FOR A SONG
g	COMES TO A HEAD	n	GO STRAIGHT

1 **PLANS TO INCREASE BUS FARES __b__**
(are revealed)

2 **MIDDLE EAST PEACE TALKS _____**
(fail to produce any results)

3 **LEADING GOVERNMENT OFFICIAL _____ OVER ACCUSATIONS OF CORRUPTION**
(becomes very angry)

4 **ROCK STAR _____ ABOUT DRUGS PROBLEM**
(confesses; tells the truth)

5 **LEAD SINGER IN NEW MUSICAL HIT _____**
(gets lots of applause)

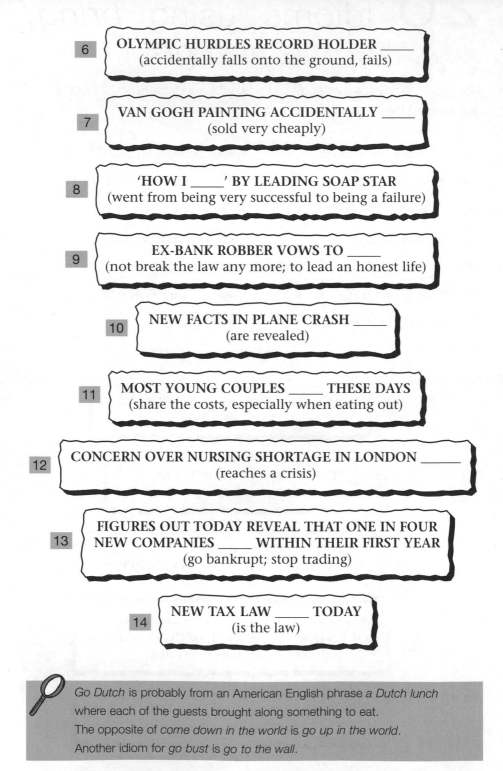

6 OLYMPIC HURDLES RECORD HOLDER _____
(accidentally falls onto the ground, fails)

7 VAN GOGH PAINTING ACCIDENTALLY _____
(sold very cheaply)

8 'HOW I _____' BY LEADING SOAP STAR
(went from being very successful to being a failure)

9 EX-BANK ROBBER VOWS TO _____
(not break the law any more; to lead an honest life)

10 NEW FACTS IN PLANE CRASH _____
(are revealed)

11 MOST YOUNG COUPLES _____ THESE DAYS
(share the costs, especially when eating out)

12 CONCERN OVER NURSING SHORTAGE IN LONDON _____
(reaches a crisis)

13 FIGURES OUT TODAY REVEAL THAT ONE IN FOUR
NEW COMPANIES _____ WITHIN THEIR FIRST YEAR
(go bankrupt; stop trading)

14 NEW TAX LAW _____ TODAY
(is the law)

Go Dutch is probably from an American English phrase *a Dutch lunch*
where each of the guests brought along something to eat.
The opposite of *come down in the world* is *go up in the world*.
Another idiom for *go bust* is *go to the wall*.

27 Idioms using *get* and *keep*

Say whether the idioms in the following sentences are used correctly (true) or incorrectly (false).

		True	False
1	If someone tells you to **get a move on** they want you to hurry.	✓	___
2	You would probably feel quite flattered if someone told you that you **got on their nerves**.	___	___
3	I always try to **keep in touch with** my friends.	___	___
4	You'll soon learn. You'll soon **get the hang of it**.	___	___
5	If you say that someone **got out of bed on the wrong side**, you mean that they are not very intelligent.	___	___
6	If something **gets your goat**, it annoys you.	___	___
7	Emotional people would find it hard to **keep a stiff upper lip**.	___	___
8	He was a poor swimmer and found it hard to **keep his head above water**.	___	___
9	He had an exam on Friday and asked me to **keep my fingers crossed** for him.	___	___
10	You would probably feel relieved if you managed to **get something off your chest**.	___	___
11	To **get wind of something** is to be told a secret.	___	___
12	To **keep something under your hat** is to deceive or cheat someone.	___	___
13	To **keep a straight face** is not to laugh, even though you feel like laughing.	___	___

14 She told her husband everything – she used
to **keep him in the dark.** _____ _____

15 Most people would feel quite proud
to **get the sack.** _____ _____

16 It was really cheap. I **got it for a song.** _____ _____

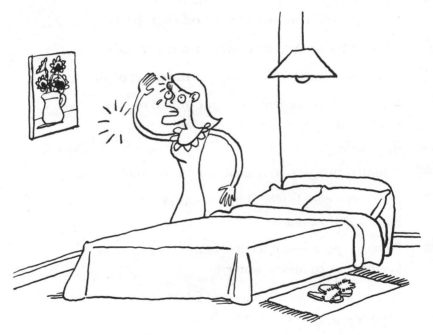

She got out of bed on the wrong side this morning.

Get one's goat comes from the time when it was common to keep a goat in
the same stable as a racehorse to calm its nerves before a big race. If,
however, someone stole the goat, the horse would become agitated and
perform badly. So the owner would probably be very angry!
In the past people believed that left was unlucky and right was lucky. So
they believed that if you put your left leg out of bed first, then things would
go wrong for you (*get out of bed on the wrong side*).

28 Idioms using *pull put* and *turn*

A For each sentence in **I** find a suitable idiom from **II**.

I

1 Dimitri wasn't being serious! He was just teasing you!

2 Jeanette really frightened Robbie when she suddenly dropped a tray behind him.

3 He spoke very bluntly to me and told me exactly what he thought about the way I was behaving.

4 Kate really annoyed Christophe when she told him he was a terrible driver.

5 My cat was so ill, the vet decided to end her suffering.

6 Mario will have to work much harder to pass his exams next summer.

7 Loren told the man standing next to him that he thought the painting was rubbish. But the man was the person who had painted it!

8 The prisoner promised never to break the law again. He was a changed man now.

II

a He put her to sleep.

b He's turned over a new leaf.

c She put his back up.

d He put his foot in it.

e He was pulling your leg!

f He didn't pull any punches.

g He needs to pull his socks up.

h She put the wind up him.

Write your answers here:

1	2	3	4	5	6	7	8
e							

B Replace the words in italics in the sentences below with an idiom from the box.

pull strings	pull the wool over someone's eyes
put a spoke in someone's wheel	put something on the map
put the cat among the pigeons	put two and two together
~~put one's foot down~~	turn a blind eye to something

1 His daughter asked to go to an all-night party, but he *firmly refused* and told her she would have to be home by midnight.

His daughter asked to go to an all-night party, but he **put his foot down** and told her she would have to be home by midnight.

2 They were going to built the highest skyscraper in the world in a bid to *make their city really famous*.

3 It was his views on whale hunting that really *caused a lot of trouble and made a lot of people very angry*.

4 He saw the young boy take the bar of chocolate without paying for it, but he decided to *ignore it*.

5 Ask your uncle to try and *use his influence and contacts* to get you the job.

6 I'm too smart for you! You can't *deceive me*!

7   When he noticed that both his wife and best friend always went out alone the same evenings every week, he *guessed the truth* and came to the conclusion that they were having an affair.

8   Tell your daughter you need the car this weekend – that'll *upset her plans*.

He got the job by pulling strings!

Spokes are the thin metal bars inside a wheel.
When a boxer *pulls his punches* he doesn't hit as hard as he could.
Another way of saying *I had my cat put to sleep* is to say *I had my cat put down*.
Leaf is an old-fashioned word for a page in a book. So when you *turn over a new leaf* (page) you have a new fresh and clean one to start writing on.

29 Idioms using various verbs

In each of the sentences below, two of the alternatives are correct. Underline the one that does **not** fit in.

1 The old man at number 10 has died. He _____ on Friday morning.

a) buried the hatchet
b) kicked the bucket
c) passed away

2 Alberto lost his temper. He _____.

a) blew his top
b) barked up the wrong tree
c) flew off the handle

3 She makes me so angry sometimes. She really _____.

a) makes my blood boil
b) leads me up the garden path
c) gets my goat

4 The butcher was very irritable this morning. He _____!

a) went like a bomb
b) bit my head off
c) was like a bear with a sore head

5 It's very wet today. It's _____.

a) bucketing down
b) beating about the bush
c) raining cats and dogs

6 I couldn't do the bungee jump in the end. I _____.

a) got cold feet
b) chickened out
c) missed the boat

7 The market trader deceived us. He _____.

a) took us for a ride
b) led us up the garden path
c) pipped us at the post

8 You said something very embarrassing. You really _____.

a) dropped a clanger
b) blew your own trumpet
c) put your foot in it

9 Juliette had a very good relationship with her mother-in-law. They _____.

a) were like two peas in a pod
b) really hit it off
c) got on like a house on fire

10 It's so expensive here. _____.

a) You have to pay through the nose for a flat.
b) Flats cost the earth.
c) You can get a flat for a song.

11 I'm tired. I think I'll _____.

a) throw in the towel
b) hit the sack
c) turn in

12 It's a lot of fuss about nothing. _____

a) They're making a mountain out of a molehill!
b) It's a flash in the pan!
c) It's just a storm in a teacup!

13 Rachael doesn't have a job at the moment. She's _____.

a) skating on thin ice
b) on the dole
c) been given the sack

14 It was supposed to be a secret, but she _____.

a) let the cat out of the bag
b) gave the game away
c) gave them a piece of her mind

15 Although they both worked, they didn't have much money and _____.

a) lived from hand to mouth
b) found it hard to make ends meet
c) were often in the doghouse

16 The film was so frightening, it _____.

a) made my hair stand on end
b) drove me up the wall
c) brought me out in a cold sweat

If someone calls you *chicken* they are calling you are a coward.

A trick in the old days was to put a cat in a bag or a sack and sell it as a pig. But if people insisted on opening the sack before buying it then the trick would be revealed (*let the cat out of the bag*).

In England during the seventeenth century there weren't any drains to take away heavy rain, so many pets and stray animals drowned during heavy downpours. So it was not unusual to see their bodies floating down the streets (*raining cats and dogs*).

30 Just for fun 3

Complete the crossword. All the idioms are found in Tests 21–29.

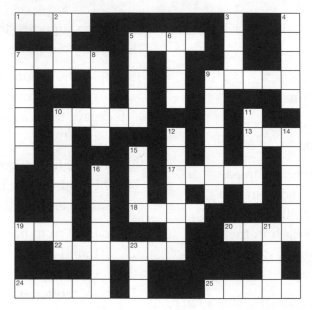

Across

1 We haven't got a timetable, so we're just going to have to take pot _____ on there being a late train tonight to Manchester.

5 Some of the first people to have Internet sites made a _____ when they sold them later to bigger companies.

7 They often turned a ____ eye to their children's naughty behaviour.

9 The man threatened William and told him to hand over his wallet. William decided to call his _____ and the man ran away.

10 Your work's not up to standard. You're going to have to pull your _____ up!

13 This is a secret, remember, so keep it under your _____.

17 Reading between the _____, it's obvious that he's not really happy in his new job.

18 The robbers managed to give the police the _____.

19 My mother never eats beef. She has a _____ in her bonnet about it causing the human form of 'mad cow' disease.

20   Fewer firms have gone _____ this year than last year. So the economy must be improving.

22   We'll have to call off the picnic. It's _____ cats and dogs!

24   Siobhan is in such a bad mood today. She must have got out of bed on the _____ side.

25   The manager was arrested for cooking the _____.

Down

2   He's always had a _____ on his shoulder about being brought up working class.

3   The way this government wastes money really makes my blood _____!

4   He wanted to cry, but kept a _____ upper lip.

5   One of the men arrested in connection with the recent bank robbery in Amsterdam decided to spill the _____ and tell the police all he knew.

6   We're late! We're going to have to get a _____ on!

7   'How old was Mr Braun when he kicked the _____?'
'At least ninety.'

8   The first time they went on a date, they went _____. The second time, Juliet paid for the meal.

9   You're _____ up the wrong tree if you think I borrowed the CDs. I wasn't even at the party.

10   I think I've upset Martine. She gave me the cold _____ this morning when I tried to explain why I hadn't turned up at the cinema last night.

11   Why don't you tell me what's bothering you? It does help, you know, to get things off your _____.

12   He wasn't being serious! He was only _____ your leg!

14   Mr Bradshaw could feel a lump in his _____ as his daughter said 'I do!' at the wedding.

15   I'll be back in a minute – I'm just going to stretch my _____.

16   How many hours a week do you think you spend _____ the Net?

21   He got the _____ for stealing, so his old boss is hardly likely to give him a reference now.

23   Do you know any good ways of breaking the _____ at a party?

Section 4:
Idioms using prepositions

This section looks at idioms that begin with or contain a preposition.

Certain prepositions occur more frequently in idioms than others, namely *at*, *by*, *for*, *in*, *on*, *off* and *out of*.

Most of the examples given here are preposition–noun/noun phrase combinations. It is perhaps worth pointing out the difference between the literal meaning of a preposition–noun phrase and the idiomatic meaning. A typical example is the following:

> *When the lights went out we were **in the dark**.*

> *I knew nothing about the plan. I was completely **in the dark**.*

The first example is literal and means 'being without light'. The second example is idiomatic and means 'I was kept ignorant. I was not told anything'.

Here are other examples of idioms found in this section:

by a hair's breadth (very narrowly, e.g. She missed having an accident by a hair's breadth.)

in deep water (be in trouble)

off the record (not official, e.g. You can't print what I say – it's off the record.)

on the dot (be precise, on time)

out of sorts (slightly ill)

Feeling out of sorts

31 Idioms using *at*

Fill in the missing words in the sentences below. The words in brackets after each sentence should help you. Choose from the following:

> at a loss   at a pinch   ~~at a rough guess~~   at a standstill
> at a stretch   at death's door   at large   at loggerheads
> at short notice   at sixes and sevens   at the crack of dawn
> at the drop of a hat   at the eleventh hour   at your wits' end   at will

1   'How many were there at the meeting last night?'

'I'm not sure exactly, but __at a rough guess__ about 300.'
(*approximately 300*)

2   Barbara and Gordon are always _____ . I can't imagine
them ever getting married. (*quarrelling*)

3   This morning's newspaper headline read: Cold Blooded Murderer
Still _____ ! (*free, not caught*)

4   You can't expect me to work overtime _____ such
_____ ! I need to be told at least a day in advance.
(*with such little advanced warning*)

5   The workers went on strike _____ . (*suddenly and
easily*)

6   Like you, I'm _____ to explain the sudden fall in share
prices. I've absolutely no idea what can have caused it. (*unable to
explain it*)

7   New evidence proving he was innocent was uncovered
_____ . (*at the last possible moment before it is too late*)

8   I've got room in the car for three people, maybe four
_____ . (*possibly four, but with some difficulty*)

9   A chameleon is a remarkable creature in that it is able to change
the colour of its skin _____ . (*when it wants to*)

10   I may be getting on a bit, but I'm certainly not _____
yet! I hope to live for at least another ten to fifteen years!
(*seriously ill; about to die*)

11   We got up _____ , as we wanted to leave London
before the traffic built up. (*very early*)

12   I'm afraid everything's _____ this week. Both the
secretaries are ill and no one knows where anything is. (*muddled, confused*)

13   Traffic was _____ this morning because of an accident
on the M25. (*not moving*)

14   When her daughter didn't come home on the last bus, Mrs Lee
was _____ . (*really worried, not knowing what to do next*)

15   The thing I don't like about my present job is that we often have to
work up to ten hours _____ . (*ten hours without stopping*)

For *at a pinch* you can also say *at a push*.
To remember *at a standstill* imagine the traffic standing still – in other words, not moving.

32 Idioms using *by* and *for*

Rewrite the sentences below, replacing the words in **bold** type with a suitable idiom. Choose from the following:

by a hair's breadth	by chance	by ear	by heart	by mistake
by no means	for good	~~for kicks~~	for love or money	for short
	for the high jump	for the time being		

1. The football hooligans admitted to smashing shop windows just **for the excitement it gave them**.

   _____ *for kicks* _____

2. If taxes continue to rise I shall leave this country **for ever**.

   _____

3. Do you like my ring? I saw it quite **unexpectedly** in the window of an antique shop while I was shopping in the Old Town.

   _____

4. This piano was a present from my grandmother and I wouldn't part with it **under any circumstances whatsoever**.

   _____

5. The government has decided to drop its plans to raise the school leaving age to eighteen – at least **for the moment**.

   _____

6. His name was Benjamin, but he was called Ben – **the short form of his name**.

   _____

7 The car swerved to avoid a cyclist and **just missed** hitting a pedestrian.

   _____

8 Mr Wilson's **going to be punished**. He's been caught fiddling the accounts.

   _____

9 Probably the only really effective way of learning prepositions is **to memorise** them.

   _____

10 He can't read a note of music – he plays everything **from memory**.

   _____

11 It is **not in the least** uncommon for squirrels to bury nuts in the autumn.

   _____

12 I was rushing this morning and **accidentally** put my jumper on back to front.

   _____

 Instead of _for good_, you can also say _for keeps_.

33 Idioms using *in*

Go from a square in the TOP ROW to a square in the BOTTOM ROW in twenty moves. You can move vertically, horizontally or diagonally. To help you trace the correct route, work out the missing words in the idioms in the sentences that follow.

jiffy	long run	tight spot	dribs and drabs	mint condition
public	dark	season	nick of time	good shape
succession	stock	red	flash	cash
cold blood	nutshell	rut	stitches	flesh
short	change	element	limelight	turns
due course	broad daylight	deep water	common	prime
bag	cold sweat	shoes	doghouse	bargain
theory	favour of	vain	time	hot water
pink	all	know	doldrums	full swing

MOVES (in this order)

1 The law may be unpopular now, but I'm sure people will soon see how good it is for the country and themselves *in the* ___*long run*___ .

2 No one's been told what's going to happen at the conference yet. We're all being kept *in the* _____ for some reason.

3 Last year was the third year *in* _____ that he had won the championships.

4 At the trial it was found that the victim had been killed *in* _____ .

5 And that *in a* _____ , ladies and gentlemen, is the government's position at the moment.

6 Although I've been trying hard to pay back my bank loan I'm still nearly £2,000 *in the* _____ . In fact, I've got to go and see my bank manager about it tomorrow.

7 Strawberries cost a lot at the moment because they're not *in* _____ .

8 The audience arrived *in* _____ , but by 7.30 the hall was completely full.

9 A coin from 1896 *in* _____ would probably fetch as much as £1,000 at an auction.

10 Although she is in her early fifties, she exercises regularly and is still *in* very _____ .

11 The answer to the examination question came to her in *a* _____ .

12 When she told us the joke about the shark and the octopus we were *in* _____ . We just couldn't stop laughing.

13 'I saw the queen yesterday *in the* _____ . She was standing as close to me as you are now.'

14 The journey to Paris was a long one, so they *took it in* _____ to drive.

15 I think I have found the perfect girlfriend at last! We have so much *in* _____ .

16 The main headline in today's *Financial Times* was: Executive *in* _____ Over Alleged Bribes!

17 The robbery happened *in* _____ in one of the busiest parts of the town.

18 The thought of getting up to make a speech in public always *brought him out in a* _____ .

19 The inexperienced teacher *tried in* _____ to control the unruly class. In the end he had to call for the headteacher.

20 Sorry if I'm not very good company today. I'm feeling a bit *in the* _____ .

The opposite of *in good shape* is *in poor shape*.

If you are feeling sad and depressed (*in the doldrums*) you can also be feeling *down in the dumps*.

In bookkeeping, sums that were owed were usually written in red ink (*in the red*).

To *kill in cold blood* is to kill without any emotions – coldly and cruelly.

34 Idioms using *on* and *off*

Complete sentences 1–12 by choosing an ending from a–l.

1 It wasn't planned. We did it …

2 Charles had short legs, so he found it hard …

3 The students were *on tenterhooks* as they …

4 I've been learning Japanese *on and off* …

5 They arranged to meet outside the cinema …

6 We just called round …

7 The two men who escaped from jail at the weekend …

8 Oh, what's that actor's name? I know it! It's …

9 Let's meet later at the church. I'll …

10 They're sending someone from head office to inspect us today …

11 I can't take any more work on. I've got enough …

12 Remember, you mustn't print any of it! What I've just told you …

'What sort of insect is that?'
'Er … it's on the tip of my tongue!'

a	is strictly *off the record*.
b	*on my plate* as it is.
c	on the *off-chance* that you were at home.
d	so we'd better be *on our toes*.
e	*on the spur of the moment*.
f	at 8.30 *on the dot*.
g	be *off duty* by then.
h	to buy clothes *off the peg*.
i	are still *on the run*.
j	for about two years now.
k	waited for their exam results.
l	*on the tip of my tongue*!

Write your answers here:

1	2	3	4	5	6	7	8	9	10	11	12
e											

In the past, freshly woven cloth was stretched on a framework called a *tenter* and held tight by small hooks known as *tenterhooks*. If you are feeling anxious, your body is often tight or tense (*on tenterhooks*).
The opposite of *off duty* is *on duty*.

35 Idioms using *out of*

Say whether the idioms in the following sentences are used correctly (true) or incorrectly (false).

		True	False
1	Enrico ran so fast that he was completely **out of breath**.	✓	
2	I can't see us beating them at tennis this year – we're so **out of practice**.		
3	You'll have to stay at a hotel, I'm afraid. We're **out of place** at the moment.		
4	The demonstration got **out of hand**, so the police were called in.		
5	It's difficult to get hold of copies of the book as it's **out of print**.		
6	This TV set is **out of condition**. I'll have to get it repaired.		
7	The advanced computer course was really difficult and I felt really **out of my depth**.		
8	She's got a lovely voice – she can really sing **out of tune**!		
9	Most people would be pleased if they found themselves **out of pocket**.		
10	No, you can't borrow my car! It's quite **out of the question**!		
11	I wasn't expecting a letter from her. It arrived quite **out of the blue**.		
12	You probably wouldn't want to go to a party if you were feeling **out of sorts**.		
13	I feel quite fit. I've been **out of the running** for the past week.		

14 This area is normally **out of bounds** for
non-members.   _____   _____

15 He's not **out of the woods** yet. He's still
very young and inexperienced.   _____   _____

16 You'd better put those tablets **out of reach**
of the children.   _____   _____

It arrived quite out of the blue.

The opposite of *out of* is often *in*, so you can *sing in tune*, *be in pocket* and
be in place.
To remember *out of pocket* imagine all your money falling out of your
pocket, so you lose a lot of money.
Out of the blue refers to lightning appearing suddenly and unexpectedly in a
blue sky.

36 Idioms using prepositions and particles

Fill in the missing prepositions or particles in the following sentences.

1   Everything seems to be __*above*__ *board*, but there's something that doesn't feel quite right. I just wish I knew what it was.

2   I always thought he was strange. After seeing him at the party I'm convinced that he's _____ *the bend*!

3   If you have any complaints, then *tell me* _____ *my face*. I can't stand people who *do things* _____ *my back*.

4   My mother is a vegetarian and won't eat meat _____ *principle*.

5   _____ *you, me and the gatepost*, I don't think the new boss will last more than a few months.

6   This work is taking much longer than I thought. _____ *this rate* it'll be Christmas before it's finished.

7   He didn't have time to prepare a speech so he had to give one _____ *the cuff*.

8   Throughout the flight he was very much _____ *edge*, and didn't start to relax until the plane had landed.

9   I wouldn't like to *be* _____ *her shoes* when Miss Hoffman finds out that she's lost the exam papers.

10 I'd love to come to the concert with you but I can't, I'm afraid. I'm _____ _____ *my ears in work* this week.

11 Playing tennis once a week is one way of *letting* _____ *steam*.

12 He learnt Portuguese _____ *scratch* in less than six months.

13 The competitors waited _____ *baited breath* for the results to be read out.

14   Mrs Samuel's daughter is terrible, isn't she? Out _____ *all hours* and never a kind word to anyone.

15   I bought a computer last year, but I've had nothing but trouble with it. As far as I'm concerned it was money _____ *the drain*!

16   The football match had to be postponed _____ *account* _____ the bad weather.

'I wouldn't like to be in her shoes!'

 A *drain* is a pipe for carrying away water. So if you dropped anything down it, you would lose it!

The *scratch* used to be a starting line which was scratched on the ground to show where a race should start from, so *from scratch* means from the start, beginning.

37 Idioms using various prepositions 1

Complete the captions by writing the letters (a–l) in the gaps. Use the pictures to help you. Choose from the following:

a	at random	g	in the limelight
b	behind bars	h	keep in touch
c	behind the times	i	off the beaten track
d	by ear	j	on fire
e	in a rut	k	out of order
f	in full swing	l	out of this world

1

He's very talented. He plays the trumpet _____*d*_____ .

2

The party was _____ when they arrived.

3

The restaurant was _____ !

4

The numbers are chosen _____ .

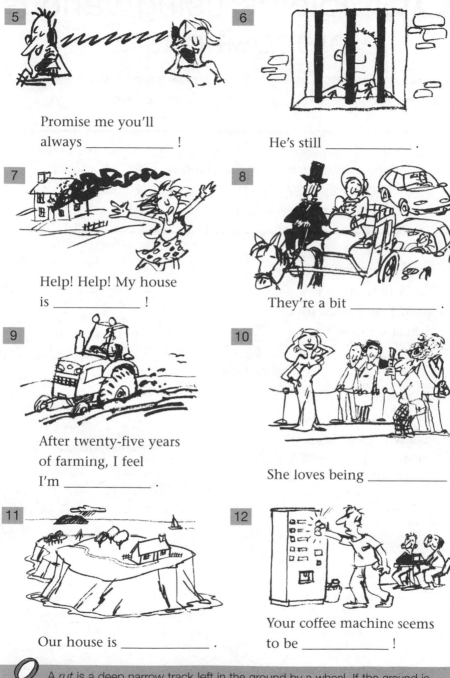

5
Promise me you'll
always _____ !

6
He's still _____ .

7
Help! Help! My house
is _____ !

8
They're a bit _____ .

9
After twenty-five years
of farming, I feel
I'm _____ .

10
She loves being _____ .

11
Our house is _____ .

12
Your coffee machine seems
to be _____ !

A *rut* is a deep narrow track left in the ground by a wheel. If the ground is
muddy, it is very easy for your car, etc. to get stuck in it (*in a rut*).
Prison windows traditionally have iron *bars* to stop a prisoner escaping. So if
you are behind them you are in a prison cell (*behind bars*)

38 Idioms using various prepositions 2

Look at what the people are saying and complete the captions, making any changes that may be necessary. Choose from the box below.

by the skin of one's teeth	by word of mouth	down in the dumps
fall off the back of a lorry	in one's birthday suit	off one's head
~~over the moon~~	up to scratch	under your hat
under the weather	up in arms	up with the lark

1
'Guess what? I've passed my exams! Isn't it great – I'm so happy!'

She's __over the moon__.

2
'You can't beat this time of day! It's so peaceful ... just the sound of the birds! I'm so glad I decided to be a milkman!'

He's _____.

3
'What's the point of living? My job's boring, my girlfriend's just left me, I'm going bald.'

He's feeling _____.

4
'And this is a photograph of Zzrump. He's an alien, you know… Comes from one of the moons of Jupiter. He often pops in for tea on a Sunday.

She must be _____.

5
'The restaurant is so cosy! And the food – I tell you, Monique, it's out of this world! The strange thing is, they don't advertise. They just rely on people telling their friends about them.'

The restaurant gets its customers _____.

6
'The car suddenly came hurtling towards me and how it didn't hit me I'll never know! I tell you – I'm lucky to be alive!'

She escaped _____.

7

'How dare they just cancel their concert like that! I've been travelling since 5 a.m. today. I tell you they can't do this! Not with just an hour to go!'

He's _____ .

8

'There's a rumour going around the embassy that the ambassador's assistant is a spy. But don't say anything!'

Keep it _____ .

9

'Do you like my new DVD player? I got it half price. I can get one for you if you like – so long as you keep quiet about it.'

The items have probably _____ .

10

'I'm sorry, but I don't think I can come to the meeting tonight. I've got this shocking cold and a bit of a temperature... I think I'd better just go to bed.'

She's feeling a bit _____ .

11

'Suddenly this guy appears and runs onto the baseball pitch! He was stark naked! Honestly! Not a stitch of clothing on! Well, the crowd went mad!'

The man was

_____ .

12

'Although she had to sit through three interviews and pass five tests before she was offered the job, within months they had sacked her and found someone better.'

She wasn't

_____ .

A *lark* is a type of brown singing bird. Birds usually start singing very early in the morning.

You are naked when you are born and the day you are born is your birthday (*in your birthday suit*). You could also have said he was *starkers*!

To remember *up in arms* imagine a group of people with their arms held in the air, shaking their fists at someone because they are very angry.

39 Idioms using various prepositions 3

Choose the best idiom (a, b or c) to complete the sentences below. To help you, the meaning of the idiom is given in brackets after each sentence.

1   We must __at all costs__ catch the 7.30 train. Otherwise we won't get to the meeting in time.

   (a) at all costs   b) at best   c) at once

   (Meaning: *We must catch it without fail.*)

2   He wasn't prepared for the question, so he was forced to answer

   _____ .

   a) on all fours   b) on the go   c) off the top of his head

   (Meaning: *without preparing beforehand; spontaneously*)

3   Christmas decorations are nice, but my neighbours have really gone _____ this year – their whole house is covered in flashing lights.

   a) over the moon   b) over the top   c) at half mast

   (Meaning: *They have done more than is necessary or suitable.*)

4   They say that when John Lennon first saw Yoko Ono it was a classic case of love _____ .

   a) at first sight   b) for keeps   c) in a jiffy

   (Meaning: *It was love from the very moment they saw each other.*)

5   Swimming is something I like and am good at. It's right _____ .

   a) in my element   b) up my street   c) in my prime

   (Meaning: *It's exactly what I like doing.*)

6   The film, which was made _____ , surprised everyone by winning three Oscars, including the one for Best Picture.

   a) under the counter   b) on the air   c) on a shoestring

   (Meaning: *on a very small budget*)

7 She passed her exam _____ !'

a) with open arms   b) with flying colours   c) with a bang

(Meaning: *She passed very easily with good grades.*)

8 The old man was very weak and was close to death. He was ____ .

a) out of his mind   b) over the hill   c) on his last legs

(Meaning: *He was dying.*)

9 The critics were unanimous that his latest book was not _____ .

a) in the bag   b) on the ball   c) up to scratch

(Meaning: *not up to the usual standard*)

10 You'll be _____ if the boss ever finds out that you forgot to deliver those parcels on time last week.

a) on the carpet   b) at fault   c) out for the count

(Meaning: *You'll be in trouble.*)

11 I wonder if you can help me, Henri? I'm _____ and don't know what to do.

a) in an ivory tower   b) in a jam   c) on the wrong track

(Meaning: *to be in trouble, difficulties*)

12 It looks as though another government resignation is _____ at the moment.

a) on the move   b) in due course   c) on the cards

(Meaning: *It is going to happen soon.*)

13 'Two tins of baked beans, please.'
'I'm afraid we haven't got any _____ at the moment. But we should be getting some more on Thursday.'

a) in stock   b) on call   c) under cover

(Meaning: *available for sale*)

14 Bjorn won't do anything without asking his wife first. She's really got him _____ .

a) under the table   b) under her thumb c) under lock and key

(Meaning: *She makes all the decisions; she is the dominant partner in the marriage.*)

15 I'm _____ whether to go to Greece for the summer or not.

a) on second thoughts   b) on the spot   c) in two minds

(Meaning: *undecided*)

'Our new striker is really on the ball!'

On the cards is probably a reference to trying to see into the future using a pack of cards. So if something is *on the cards,* it's likely to happen in the near future.

Over the top is sometimes abbreviated to 'OTT'.

40 Just for fun 4

Complete the crossword. All the idioms are found in Tests 31–39.

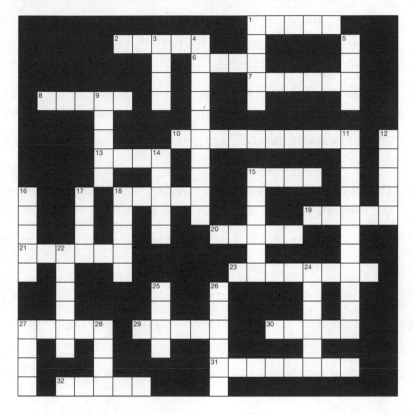

Across

1   I wouldn't like to be in your _____ when Mr Rosenthal finds out what you did to his car.

2   They smashed all the windows of the empty house just for _____ .

6   He slipped as he was crossing the road and a motorbike just missed him by a _____ 's breadth.

7   She tried hard to remember the name of the hotel – it was on the tip of her _____ .

8   I've got too much on my _____ at the moment. I've really got to learn to say no when people offer me work.

10 The traffic was at a _____ this morning as half the people living in the city left for their summer holidays.

13 The car's in _____ condition. It's only had one owner and hasn't gone more than 2,000 miles.

15 Do you think it's a good idea to get married on the _____ of the moment? Shouldn't we wait until we know each other better?

18 The musical was dreadful. As far as I'm concerned it was money down the _____ !

19 They were lucky enough to see the film star in the _____ as she left through the back entrance of the studios.

20 I find one of the best ways of letting off _____ is to go jogging.

21 He was on the _____ for being late for work again.

23 She was so funny! She had us in _____ all night.

27 He was arrested and charged with carrying out a killing in cold _____ .

29 The computers were being sold so cheaply that they must have fallen off the back of a _____ !

30 She was in two _____ about taking the job in Geneva.

31 Can you just tell us in a _____ the differences between an eclipse of the moon and an eclipse of the sun.

32 There's room for three more in the van – four at a _____ .

Down

1 I think I'll have an early night. I'm feeling a bit out of _____ .

3 She had no time to prepare a speech, so she did it off the _____ .

4 The local radio company was being run on a _____ .

5 The new teacher certainly keeps the children on their _____ ! I don't think I've seen them work so hard before.

9   Oscar does everything his wife tells him to do. He's really under her _____ .

11   My father and I are always at _____ . We just don't seem to agree on anything.

12   The news quickly spread by word of _____ .

14   He gave them a very detailed map, as his house was a bit off the beaten _____ .

15   I've got to apply for this job. It's right up my _____ .

16   Don't forget to keep in _____ when you move to Venice.

17   You're going to be for the high _____ when the boss finds out you've been stealing from the stores.

18   The course was too advanced. She felt completely out of her _____ .

22   When you play bingo, the numbers are chosen at _____ .

24   We drove to the town centre on Sunday on the off_____ that one or two shops were open.

25   He was over the _____ when he got a new car for his eighteenth birthday.

26   She passed her final exams with _____ colours.

27   The governor's resignation came completely out of the _____ . Everyone was really surprised.

28   The taxi arrived to take them to the airport at the crack of _____ .

Section 5: 'Special category' idioms

This section looks at special categories of idioms, that is idioms which are linked either by subject area or structure.

It starts by examining idioms connected with parts of the body. These are perhaps the most common and numerous of all idioms. Indeed, there seems to be an idiom for almost every part of the body, from the brain to the tongue! Examples are: *get off on the wrong foot* (make a bad start) and *cost an arm and a leg* (be very expensive).

Next are idioms to do with colour, e.g. *be black and blue* (be covered with bruises), *paint the town red* (have a good time) and idioms to do with *animals*, e.g. *have butterflies in one's stomach* (be very nervous) and *as the crow flies* (to travel in a straight, direct line from one place to the other).

Similes are another common feature of idiomatic English where one thing is compared with another using either 'as ... as' or 'like'. These comparisons are often very difficult to guess (e.g. *as keen as mustard*; *as dead as a doornail*) and have to be learnt by heart. Idioms with 'like' are slightly more difficult to understand, e.g. *like a bear with a sore head* (be in a bad mood).

This section ends with a test on proverbs. Although not so common nowadays as they used to be, they are still used widely and worth knowing. Proverbs usually contain a wise message or moral, e.g. *Beggars can't be choosers* (if you are in need, you can't have what you want – you have to accept what is given to you).

'Jack's always had green fingers, you know!'

41 Parts of the body idioms 1

Complete the definitions below with a suitable part of the body. Choose from the following words:

> brain   chin   ear   ears   eye   eyes   face   hair   ~~head~~
> lips   nose   teeth   tongue   tongue-in-cheek   tooth

1 If you're trying to do something but are getting nowhere, you might say that you're *banging your __head__ against a brick wall.*

2 If you are only joking when you say something (you don't really mean it), then it is said _____-in-_____ .

3 If you think someone is talking about you, then you might feel that *your _____ are burning.*

4 People who *have a sweet _____* like things like chocolate, ice cream, cakes, etc.

5 If someone asks you to do something and you refuse to listen or ignore it, then you *turn a deaf _____ to it.*

6 If you want help from someone for a problem you're working on, you might ask if you can *pick their _____ .*

7 If you promise to keep a secret, you might say: '*My _____ are sealed!*'

8 If you are feeling really sad you might *cry your _____ out.*

9 If you say something that is completely untrue then you are *lying through your _____ .*

10 If you are trying to cheer someone up or encourage them after they have had a bad time, you might say: '_____ up! Things can only get better!'

11 If you were trying to find out things about other people they might think you were *poking your _____ into their business.*

12 If someone was looking really sad or depressed, you might think they *had a _____ as long as a fiddle.*

13 If you are too shy to speak or have stopped talking for some reason, someone might say to you: 'What's the matter? Have you *lost your _____ ?'*

14 If someone is very angry with you and you want them to calm down, you might say: 'All right! *Keep your _____ on!'*

15 If you are in a restaurant and you want to pay your bill, you will first have to *catch the waiter's _____ .*

You can also *turn a blind eye to something* when you ignore what you have seen.

Notice how the word *nose* is often used in idioms where a person is inquisitive (*nosy, Nosy Parker, poke your nose into something*, etc.).

A *fiddle* is another word for 'violin'.

42 Parts of the body idioms 2

What's the missing idiom? To find out, decide whether the idioms in the following sentences are used correctly or not. Transfer the letter under T (for *true*) and F (for *false*) to the appropriate box on the next page.

		T	F	Box No
1	Jolene didn't want to be friendly with him, so she **kept him at arm's length**.	O	E	3
2	It was so cold outside, **it made my flesh creep**.	O	H	9
3	She really spoils her son. She **waits on him hand over fist**.	H	N	18
4	Relax! **Put your foot down**!	O	A	20
5	She'll do anything for me. I've got her **in the palm of my hand**.	I	O	6
6	Anastasia was feeling ill. She **had her heart in her mouth**.	I	K	12
7	We were really wet. We were **soaked to the skin**.	H	I	16
8	It is very easy to **lose heart** when things go wrong.	R	T	23
9	He's very nosy. He **has a finger in every pie**!	T	L	2
10	The old lady offered to tell his fortune. She offered to **grease his palm**.	G	R	14
11	He's got football **on the brain**. That's all he ever thinks about.	T	A	21
12	Mr Southgate is very generous and is always **giving** his grandchildren **the elbow**.	E	O	4
13	I'm so happy! I've fallen **head over heels** in love!	I	R	10
14	We started badly. We **got off on the wrong foot**.	E	N	13

		T	F	Box No
15	I was feeling so angry! I really **had my back to the wall!**	T	A	17
16	Celeste is a realist. She has **both feet on the ground.**	E	S	22
17	He was so tired he **ate his heart out.**	W	T	15
18	I really regret not buying those shares now! I've been **kicking my heels** all day!	N	C	11
19	The car had **changed hands** three times before he bought it.	S	N	7
20	I hate taking risks, so I rarely **stick my neck out.**	W	C	19
21	Yusef was really pleased when his boss **gave him a piece of his mind.**	M	T	8
22	I'm so busy! I'm really **run off my feet** at the moment!	D	L	5
23	She was so frightened she nearly **jumped out of her skin.**	B	S	1

Here is the missing idiom.

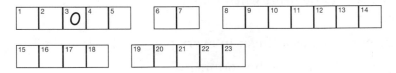

CLUE: *It means that family relationships are more important than anything else!*

Have a finger in every pie is usually used negatively, suggesting that you think the person in question has too much influence.

The opposite of to *have both feet on the ground* is to *have your head in the clouds*.

Another idiom for *give someone the elbow* is *give someone the brush-off*.

To *get off on the wrong foot* is a reference to the fact that when marching, soldiers have to start on the same foot.

43 Parts of the body idioms 3

Complete the newspaper headlines with a suitable idiom from below. Write the correct letter (a–o) in the gaps. Choose from the following:

a	AT FIRST HAND
b	COST AN ARM AND A LEG
c	FALL ON DEAF EARS
d	FOOT THE BILL
e	GET THEIR FINGERS BURNT
f	HAND IN GLOVE
g	KEEP THEIR HEADS ABOVE WATER
h	KEEPS HER HEAD
i	LIFT A FINGER
j	PUT THEIR SHOULDERS TO THE WHEEL
k	SAVES HIS SKIN
l	SEE EYE TO EYE
m	THUMBED A LIFT
n	TOOTH AND NAIL
o	TRY HIS HAND AT

1

UNITED NATIONS SECRETARY GENERAL'S
PLEAS FOR CALM __c__
(are ignored)

2

TV JOURNALIST ACCUSES POLICE COMMISSIONER OF
BEING _____ WITH NOTORIOUS SOHO GANG LEADER
(very friendly with; closely associated with)

3

CAR MANUFACTURER URGES WORKFORCE TO _____
(make a greater effort; work harder)

4

ITALY'S NATIONAL TEAM PROMISE FANS TO FIGHT _____
TO WIN REPLAY IN BARCELONA
(fight fiercely)

5

GOVERNMENT REFUSES TO _____ TO
HELP SINGLE MOTHERS
(do anything)

6

FAMOUS POP STAR TO _____ ACTING
(try doing something new, namely acting)

7

NEW HOUSES IN TOWN CENTRE TO _____
(be very expensive to buy)

8

TEENAGER WHO _____ HOME FROM DISCO
FOUND DEAD AT SIDE OF MOTORWAY
(hitchhiked)

9

PILOT _____ AND LANDS DAMAGED PLANE
SUCCESSFULLY
(remains calm)

10

GOVERNMENT AND TEACHERS' UNIONS DON'T _____
OVER NEW EDUCATION REPORT
(agree; have the same opinion)

11

NEW REPORT: AVERAGE FAMILIES STRUGGLING TO _____
(keep out of debt, manage financially)

12

TAXPAYERS TO _____ FOR NEW ARTS AND
ENTERTAINMENT CENTRE
(pay the costs of)

13

SMALL SAVERS _____ AS BANK COLLAPSES
(suffer financially)

14

DICTATOR _____ BY FLEEING COUNTRY
(escapes from death)

15

DUTCH TV CREW WITNESSES MASSACRE
IN MACAU _____
(directly)

To remember *keep your head above water*, imagine you are swimming. If your head goes below the water you can get into difficulties and drown. The only way to survive is to keep your head above the surface of the water. Other idioms for *cost an arm and a leg* are *cost a fortune* and *cost a pretty penny*.

44 Colour idioms

A Match the idioms on the left with the correct definitions on the right.

1	a black sheep	**a**	a very important or joyful occasion in your life (e.g. your wedding anniversary)
2	grey matter	**b**	something that has cost a lot of money but has no useful purpose
3	a green belt	**c**	intelligence
4	a red herring	**d**	an unimportant lie, usually told so as not to hurt someone's feelings
5	a red-letter day	**e**	something that takes people's attention away from the main subject being talked or written about
6	red tape	**f**	an area of fields and woodland around a town or city
7	a white elephant	**g**	a member of the family who is bad in the eyes of the rest of the family
8	a white lie	**h**	official rules which do not seem necessary and which make things happen very slowly; unnecessary bureaucracy

Write your answers here:

1	2	3	4	5	6	7	8
g							

B Complete the idioms in the following sentences with a suitable colour. Choose from *black*, *blue*, *green*, *pink*, *red*, *white* and *yellow*. You can use the same colour more than once.

1 After several weeks of discussion, the group were **given the
___green___ light**, and could finally go ahead with the new project. (*They were given permission to go ahead.*)

2 There's no point in asking my boss for a day off next week. I'm **in her _____ books**. (*I'm not very popular with her at the moment.*)

3 Bernardine has always **had _____ fingers**. That's why her garden looks so good. (*She has always been good at gardening.*)

4 You can argue with her **until you're _____ in the face**. But once she's made up her mind, that's it! (*It doesn't matter what you say to her, she won't listen to you.*)

5 After a neighbour raised the alarm, the burglar was **caught _____ -handed** by the police. (*He was caught as he was committing the crime.*)

6 If there was a war, I don't think I'd fight for my country. I've **got too much of a _____ streak**. I'd be afraid of getting killed. (*I'm too much of a coward.*)

7 Her husband always **saw _____** when the neighbours played loud music. (*He became very angry.*)

8 By the way, Maurice, my wife **was tickled _____** at your asking her to judge the Flower Show. (*She was very amused and pleased.*)

9 I'm not going to play rugby again! I **was _____ and _____ all over** after the last match. (*Covered with bruises.*)

10 All the girls **were _____ with envy** when Natasha told her that Viktor Borowitz had asked her out. (*They were very envious.*)

11 After passing their final exams, the students decided to **paint the town** _____ . (*They decided to go out and have a good time.*)

12 In most countries, goods that are scarce or illegal can usually be obtained **on the** _____ **market.** (*From unofficial, usually illegal sources.*)

13 My mother always goes **as** _____ **as a beetroot** whenever she's embarrassed. (*She blushes.*)

14 She **gave her son a** _____ **look** to show she was annoyed with the way he was behaving. (*She looked angrily at him.*)

15 Now that Alfonso's parents have moved to Madrid, he only sees them **once in a** _____ **moon.** (*He sees them very infrequently.*)

16 The company was **in the** _____ for the first time since it was founded. (*The company owed money; had made a loss.*)

Legend has it that a rare white elephant in ancient Thailand automatically became the king's property. It was considered sacred and never put to work. The king didn't always keep such elephants, however. If someone displeased him, he would give them a white elephant as a gift, knowing that the animal would be so expensive to keep that it would eventually ruin its owner.

To *catch someone red-handed* probably refers to the discovery of a murderer so soon after committing the crime that blood is still on his or her hands.

45 Animal idioms 1

What do the following animal idioms mean? Choose the best answer (a, b or c).

1 From here to Cardiff is about fifty kilometres **as the crow flies**.

a) if you go by plane
b) if you travel in a straight line *(circled)*
c) if you travel by motorway

2 You need to be **an early bird** in this job.

a) get up early in the morning
b) be able to make decisions quickly
c) be very active

3 I haven't seen my old school friend for **donkey's years**.

a) since we left school
b) for ten years exactly
c) for a very long time

4 Beatriz always **gets butterflies in her stomach** before visiting the dentist.

a) has diarrhoea
b) feels ill
c) feels very nervous

5 I don't mind helping her, but what **gets my goat** is that she never thanks me.

a) makes me cry
b) annoys me
c) hurts me

6 When I went to school we used to learn poems **parrot-fashion**.

a) by repeating them continuously
b) by writing them down many times
c) very quickly

7 What's wrong with Gavin today? He's **like a cat on hot bricks**.

a) He looks as though he's in pain.
b) He's in a very bad mood.
c) He's very restless and nervous.

8 I've warned her about the dangers of smoking thousands of times, but it's like **water off a duck's back**.

a) She only takes notice for a short while.
b) She just thinks I'm being very bossy.
c) It has no effect on her.

9 It's true, I tell you! Marie-Claude is getting married on Saturday. I got it **straight from the horse's mouth**!

a) I heard about it from the local gossip.
b) Her parents told me.
c) She told me herself.

10 That country has **gone to the dogs** since the new party came to power.

a) become a nation of animal lovers

b) become a lot worse

c) improved a lot

11 Pass me a glass of water, please. I've got **a frog in my throat**.

a) My voice is very husky, so I can't speak clearly.

b) I've got a sore throat.

c) I'm very thirsty.

12 You could have **knocked me down with a feather** when my wife told me she was having twins!

a) I was so upset and angry.

b) I was so happy.

c) I was so surprised.

13 I wouldn't like to live in Zöe's flat. There's **no room to swing a cat**.

a) It smells a lot.

b) It's very small.

c) You're not allowed to have pets.

14 It's Kristin's **hen party** on Friday. You are coming, I hope?

a) a special party for someone leaving a job

b) an all-female party for a woman about to be married

c) a thirtieth birthday party

15 He really **made a pig of himself** at the staff party.

a) ate too much

b) got drunk

c) was very rude

A donkey's *ears* are very long, so the phrase *donkey's years* is probably based on this.

The most reliable way of ageing a horse was to look at its teeth. So if you wanted to buy a horse, the best way of making sure you weren't being cheated was to examine the teeth yourself (*straight from the horse's mouth*).

46 Animal idioms 2

Choose the animal (a, b or c) which best completes each idiom. To help you, the meaning of the idiom is given in brackets after each sentence.

1 What's wrong with Paul today? He's **like** _a bear_ **with a sore head!**

a) a pig   (b) a bear   c) an ostrich

(Meaning: *He's in a very bad mood.*)

2 I love tennis. I could watch it **till** _____ **come home!**

a) the cows   b) the pigeons   c) the ducks

(Meaning: *I could watch it for a very long time without getting bored.*)

3 Turning up half an hour late for the interview really **cooked his** _____ .

a) chicken   b) lamb   c) goose

(Meaning: *It put an end to or ruined his chance of getting the job.*)

4 After years of commuting ninety miles to London, he decided to **get out of the** _____ **race** and bought a small farm in Yorkshire.

a) hen   b) rat   c) monkey

(Meaning: *To leave the constant struggle for success in business or one's job.*)

5 You're upset now, I know. But you'll soon forget her. After all, **there are plenty more** _____ **in the sea!**

a) fish   b) flies   c) sharks

(Meaning: *There are still lots of people left to have a relationship with.*)

6 He was a very timid person who **wouldn't say boo to a** _____ .

a) bat   b) goose   c) bull

(Meaning: *He was very shy.*)

7   When their grandmother died, Pieter got the _____ **share of** her money.

a) whale's   b) elephant's   c) lion's

(Meaning: *He got the largest share.*)

8   He took all the praise even though we had done most of the _____ **work.**

a) bear   b) camel   c) donkey

(Meaning: *The hard, tiring and boring work involved in a task.*)

9   The computer Max's father gave us isn't exactly the latest model, but you shouldn't **look a gift** _____ **in the mouth!** We certainly couldn't have afforded to buy one ourselves.

a) lion   b) horse   c) pig

(Meaning: *You shouldn't criticize or be ungrateful for something that has been given to you.*)

10   Adele's dog Buster looks fierce, but she says he **wouldn't hurt a** _____ !

a) fly   b) mouse   c) cat

(Meaning: *He is very gentle.*)

11   Your daughter should go in for politics, Mrs Schwartz. She can certainly **talk the hind legs off a** _____ !

a) horse   b) tiger   c) donkey

(Meaning: *She can talk for a very long time.*)

12   I don't think you fooled Beth for a minute! **There are no** _____ **on her**, you know!

a) moths   b) flies   c) spiders

(Meaning: *She is intelligent and able to think quickly.*)

13 Have you seen the latest digital camcorder – it's **the _____ knees!** I can't wait to get one.

a) bee's   b) goat's   c) pig's

(Meaning: *It's extremely good.*)

14 You can't possibly go to the party like that! You **look like something the _____ has dragged in!**

a) dog   b) cat   c) tiger

(Meaning: *You look untidy and badly dressed.*)

15 'How old is Beatrice?'

'I'm not sure, but she's certainly **no spring _____** !'

a) lamb   b) chicken   c) sparrow

(Meaning: *She's certainly not very young.*)

16 As the flu epidemic struck, people starting **dropping like _____** .

a) birds   b) insects   c) flies

(Meaning: *They started falling ill in great numbers.*)

The *lion's share* comes from one of Aesop's Fables. In the story the lion claims three-quarters of what has been caught – the biggest share.
Another idiom for *the bee's knees* is *the cat's whiskers*.
Parrots are colourful birds that can learn to talk by copying what they hear – but without understanding anything. People who learn something *parrot-fashion* don't always understand what they are learning.

47

SECTION 5

Idioms of comparison 1

Choose the word or phrase (a, b or c) which best completes each sentence.

1 Nothing ever seems to bother Steve. No matter what happens, he always remains *as cool as* _a cucumber_ .
a) cold feet   (b) a cucumber   c) an Eskimo

2 That snake can't bite you! It's *as dead as* _____ .
a) a doornail   b) a funeral   c) a brick

3 You'll have to shout, I'm afraid. My father's *as deaf as* _____ .
a) a stone   b) a politician   c) a post

4 It's hard to believe that Yanek and Stefan are brothers, isn't it? They're as *different as* _____ .
a) milk from honey   b) chalk and cheese   c) margarine from butter

5 Ever since I gave up smoking, I've felt *as fit as* _____ .
a) a fighter   b) a frog   c) a fiddle

6 I know our dog looks very ferocious, but don't worry, Liz, Fido's *as gentle as* _____ – especially with children.
a) snowflakes   b) washing-up liquid   c) a lamb

7 The children behaved well for the babysitter. They were *as good as* _____ !
a) God   b) angels   c) gold

8 He might look kind and sympathetic, but deep down he's *as hard as* _____ .
a) nails   b) a mountain   c) an iceberg

9 What on earth have you got in your suitcase – a dead body? It's *as heavy as* _____ .
a) an elephant   b) lead   c) a corpse

10 Brigitte was *as keen as* _____ to start her new belly-dancing course.
a) coffee   b) mustard   c) vinegar

11 Jasmine can't have emigrated to Canada! I saw her last night at Tamara's party *as large as* _____ !
a) a villa   b) the universe   c) life

12   'The box isn't too heavy, is it?'
'No, it's *as light as* _____ '
a) a feather   b) dust   c) lightning

13   Everyone had heard the joke about the chicken that crossed the road. It was *as old as* _____ .
a) Solomon   b) the hills   c) the dinosaurs

14   Of course Benny loves you! It's *as plain as* _____ !
a) a pancake   b) the knob on your door   c) the nose on your face

15   Justine is feeling a bit under the weather today, but I expect she'll be *as right as* _____ by the weekend.
a) sunshine   b) roses   c) rain

16   Buying shares in this company is *as safe as* _____ . There's no way you can lose your money!
a) Sunday   b) houses   c) a bank

17   I'll never eat as much as that again! I was *as sick as* _____ on my way home!
a) a pig   b) a dog   c) a horse

18   Ask Jan to give you a hand moving the furniture. He's *as strong as* _____ .
a) a horse   b) a camel   c) a donkey

19   As students, Michaela, Emily and Sue-Ellen were *as thick as* _____ .
a) thistles   b) dry leaves   c) thieves

20   After her illness she looked *as thin as* _____ !
a) a wire   b) a rake   c) a stick insect

As gentle as a lamb is usually used to refer to people or a large animal.
As good as gold is normally used to describe a well-behaved child.
As hard as nails is used to describe a person rather than an object.
You can also say *as dead as a dodo*.

48 Idioms of comparison 2

In the sentences below, the idioms of comparison (in **bold**) have got mixed up. Sort out which sentence these words really belong to.

1   I'm always asking my son to keep his room tidy, but he never listens. It's *like talking to* **a log**.

2   If Ms Fuhr ever finds out that you cheated in the exam she'll *come down on you like* **a bomb**.

3   Everything was so new in her new job that at first Alexa *felt like* **a sore thumb**.

4   We'd better get some extra food in if your brother's coming to stay with us. He *eats like* **a sieve**.

5   'Is the dress too big?'

    'No, not at all. It *fits like* **a leaf**.'

6   From the moment they first met, they *got on like* **a duck to water**.

7   She was so tired that as soon as her head touched the pillow she *went out like* **a ton of bricks**.

8   Joshua never remembers anything. He's *got a memory like* **a glove**.

9   I've lived here all my life, so I *know this area like* **a fish out of water**.

10 Their new book is *selling like* **dirt** and is bound to be another best-seller.

11 Mrs Perone was so frightened that she was *shaking like* **a light**.

12 He was so tired last night that he *slept like* **a horse** until ten o'clock this morning.

13 Normally she smoked about ten cigarettes a day, but whenever she was worried or nervous, she *smoked like* **wildfire**.

14 News of the new computer virus *spread like* **a house on fire**.

15 You can't build a skyscraper in the middle of a typical English village. It will *stick out like* **a brick wall**.

16 Although she had never tried skiing before, she *took to it like* **the back of my hand**.

17 I'm not surprised she finally divorced her husband. He used to *treat her like* **a chimney**.

18 My new car is so fast. It *goes like* **hot cakes**.

Write your answers here:

1	2	3	4	5	6	7	8	9	10	11	12	13	14	15	16	17	18
15																	

'Yes, it's perfect! It fits like a glove!'

 A *sieve* is found in the kitchen. It has small holes in it and is used for straining food.

49 Proverbs

A Take one word from each column (A, B, C and D) to form eight well-known English proverbs.

	A	B	C	D
1	Beggars	smoke	first	leap.
2	Better	sleeping	be	gained.
3	Still	ventured	you	lie.
4	Let	waters	nothing	served.
5	Look	can't	dogs	never.
6	First	before	than	fire.
7	Nothing	late	without	deep.
8	No	come	run	choosers.

Write your answers here:

1 _Beggars can't be choosers._

2 _____

3 _____

4 _____

5 _____

6 _____

7 _____

8 _____

B   Unscramble the words to form a further ten well-known proverbs. To help you, there is a clue under each proverb.

1   louder *Actions* words speak than

Actions speak louder than words

Stop talking about what you intend to do – just do it!

2   chickens hatched count they're before your *Don't*

_____

Someone promised to buy your computer from you, so you went and bought a new one. That person has just phoned to say he has changed his mind.

3   iron while hot is *Strike* the

_____

'This company is really on the up. The shares are very low now, but they won't be for long. So if I were you I'd buy as many shares as possible.'

4   twice bitten shy *Once*

_____

You bought £9,000 worth of shares. The company has now gone bust and you have lost all your money. You probably won't invest in shares again.

5   while *Make* shines hay sun the

_____

He knew it always rained during the week-long tennis tournament, so he set up a stall just outside the railway station where he sold umbrellas. He managed to sell quite a few!

6   turn another good *One* deserves

_____

He helped her move to her new flat. After all, she had helped him when he moved.

7   as is miss a good mile *A* as

_____

'I actually got three numbers right in last night's National Lottery and the other three were just one lower than the ones that won.'

'So what? You still didn't win anything, did you?'

8   many spoil *Too* the cooks broth

_____

When too many of us try to do the same thing we get in each other's way.

9   the in is bush bird two *A* worth the in hand

_____

You know your savings in the bank are safe. But if you take all your money out and invest it in something else, then it's possible to lose a lot of money as well as gain it. Is it really worth the risk?

10   way a *Where* there's will a there's

_____

If we try hard enough, we'll find a solution to the problem in the end.

Proverbs often have opposites. *Too many cooks spoil the broth* has the opposite *many hands make light work*.

If a blacksmith didn't strike the metal (often iron) he was working with at the right moment, the iron would cool and he would have to reheat it (*strike while the iron is hot*).

50 Just for fun 5

Look at the drawings below. Which idioms do they remind you of? They are all found in Tests 41–49. The words in the box should help you.

burning   catch/eye   face/fiddle   fight   finger/pie   head/water
look/leap   ~~make/pig~~   party   pick/brain   race   sealed
stick/neck   straight/mouth   strong

1 *make a pig of yourself*

Section 6: 'Special topics' idioms

This is the last section in the book and it concentrates on topic-based idioms, such as idioms to do with *health* and *illness, money, emotions, food, countries and places, crime, movement* and *travel*.

Here are some examples:

be fighting fit (be very healthy)

feel under the weather (feel slightly ill)

be rolling in it (be very rich; have lots of money)

be hopping mad (be very angry)

go as red as a beetroot (to blush)

go Dutch (share the costs, especially at a restaurant)

cook the books (falsify the bookkeeping in order to steal money)

off the beaten track (somewhere that is not very easy to reach)

The book ends with one test using idioms as responses, i.e. idioms you use when reacting to something someone has said, e.g. *You're kidding!*

Finally, the last test is a light-hearted look at idioms used in jokes and cartoons.

'She must be rolling in it.'

51 Idioms to do with health and illness

Complete the crossword by filling in the missing words in the idioms below. An explanation of each idiom is given in brackets after each clue.

Across

1 to be fighting _____ (to be extremely healthy)

4 as right as _____ (completely healthy, especially after an illness)

5 to feel _____ down (to feel tired and unhealthy)

6 to look the _____ of health (to be in very good health)

8 to be given a _____ bill of health (to be told officially that you are in good health)

9   to look like _____ warmed up (to look very tired or ill)

11   not _____ in the head (to be mentally ill; crazy)

13   still going _____ (still active and in good health)

15   to be up and _____ (to be well enough to walk about after you have been in bed because of an illness or an accident)

16   to be on your last _____ (to be very ill and likely to die soon)

17   hanging by a _____ (to be in a very dangerous situation and close to death)

Down

2   to take a _____ for the worse/better (to become worse, to become better)

3   to feel under the _____ (to feel slightly ill; not to be as well as usual)

5   to _____ your batteries (to get back your strength and energy again)

6   to feel below _____ or not to be up to _____ (to feel a little ill or lacking in energy)

7   to _____ a cold (to become ill with a cold)

10   to feel out of _____ (not feeling very well)

12   to have one foot in the _____ (to be very old or very ill)

14   to lay someone to _____ (to bury someone)

52 Idioms to do with money

In each of the sentences below, two of the alternatives are correct. Circle the one that does **not** fit in.

1 Could you lend me some money? I'm _____ .

a) a bit hard up

b) in the doldrums

c) a bit short at the moment

2 He was getting money dishonestly. He was _____ .

a) lining his pockets

b) on the fiddle

c) in a flap

3 They've got lots of money. They are _____ .

a) rolling in it

b) on the up and up

c) really well off

4 The bill is £50. Shall I pay or _____ .

a) is it on the house?

b) shall we go halves?

c) should we split the difference?

5 Alfonso used to be rich and successful once, but since his wife died his luck has changed and now he _____ .

a) is at sixes and sevens

b) is struggling to make ends meet

c) lives from hand to mouth

6 She was given money not to talk to the police. _____

a) She was given hush money.

b) She got pin money.

c) She took a backhander.

7 If something is very expensive, we say that it _____ .

a) costs an arm and a leg

b) is cheap at the price

c) costs a bomb

8 He didn't have any money. He _____ .

a) was broke

b) didn't have a penny to his name

c) was in the black

9 If you manage to buy something very cheaply, you can say you got it _____ .

a) on a shoestring

b) dirt cheap

c) for a song

10 He _____ on the stock market.

a) made a killing

b) struck it rich

c) hit the roof

11 Jack's leaving tomorrow. Let's _____ .

a) all chip in and buy him a present

b) take him to the cleaners

c) have a whip-round for him

12 They left the restaurant, leaving me to _____ .

a) hit the jackpot

b) pick up the tab

c) foot the bill

13 What do you mean 'Can I borrow £500?'. _____ , you know!

a) Money doesn't grow on trees

b) I wasn't born with a silver spoon in my mouth

c) I need to spend a penny

14 Carlotta had to pay a lot more for the goods than they were really worth. _____ .

a) She spent money like water!

b) It was daylight robbery!

c) It was a rip-off!

15 Times are getting harder. Even ordinary families nowadays are starting to _____ .

a) feel the pinch

b) hold the purse strings

c) tighten their belts

 Two other idioms you can use when you say that something costs a lot are *cost a packet* and *cost the earth*.

Tab is another word for the bill at a restaurant.

53 Idioms to do with emotions

Below are thirty-two idioms, each of which can be associated with one of the headings on the next page. Try to place each idiom under the appropriate heading – four under each, then write sentences using each of the idioms.

avoid someone like the plague	be all at sea
be as miserable as sin	~~be as pleased as Punch~~
be at sixes and sevens	be browned-off
be downhearted	be gobsmacked
be hopping mad	be hot under the collar
be in a cold sweat	be in seventh heaven
be keyed up	be like a cat on hot bricks
be on tenterhooks	be on top of the world
be out of one's depth	be rooted to the spot
be scared to death	be thrilled to bits
cut someone down to size	go as white as a sheet
go off at the deep end	go spare
have a go at someone	have a long face
have something on one's mind	not believe one's eyes
That's a turn-up for the books!	tear someone off a strip
not knowing whether you're coming or going	
You could have knocked me down with a feather!	

Feeling happy

be as pleased as Punch

_____

_____

_____

Feeling sad/fed up

_____

_____

_____

_____

Feeling frightened/shocked

_____

_____

_____

_____

Feeling worried/anxious/nervous

_____

_____

_____

_____

Feeling confused/uncertain

_____

_____

_____

_____

Feeling angry

_____

_____

_____

_____

Feeling quarrelsome/unfriendly

_____

_____

_____

_____

Feeling surprised

_____

_____

_____

_____

When you are afraid you often can't move (*rooted to the spot*).

Another idiom for *browned-off* is *cheesed off*.

To be *in seventh heaven* comes from the Jewish system of belief that there were seven heavens in ascending order of excellence. (The Muslims have a similar belief.)

54 Idioms to do with food

Complete the idioms in the sentences below using a word connected with food. The meaning of the idiom is given in brackets after each sentence. Choose from the following:

apple	apple-pie	bacon	bananas	beetroot	butter
cake	cauliflower	chew	~~cup of tea~~	egg	grapes
hot cakes	jam	onions	picnic	pie	

1 I don't like opera. **It's not really my** ___cup of tea___ . (*It's not something I really like or enjoy.*)

2 She's so clumsy and is always dropping things. She's a real _____ **fingers**! (*A very clumsy person.*)

3 Patrice tells me my new laptop isn't that good. But I'm sure it's only **sour** _____ as I know he'd like one but can't afford it. (*He's only pretending not to like it because he can't have it himself.*)

4 Your father's going to **go** _____ when he finds out what you've done to the car! (*He's going to be really angry.*)

5 **It's no** _____ finding a job these days – especially with the high unemployment rates. (*It's not a very easy job.*)

6 The band's new CD only came out yesterday, yet it's **selling like** _____ . (*It's selling quickly and in large numbers.*)

7 She really loved her grandson. He was **the** _____ **of her eye.** (*He was someone she really loved, her favourite relative.*)

8 To some people, learning a foreign language is **as easy as** _____ . To others, it is really difficult. (*It is very easy.*)

9 The money my uncle left me in his will has certainly **saved my**
_____ . I don't know how I'd have managed without it.
(*It has helped me get out of a very difficult situation.*)

10 You can usually tell a boxer from his _____ **ears**. (*Ears
that have been hit so much they are permanently swollen and a strange
shape.*)

11 I've got too much work to do at the moment. I think I may have
bitten off more than I can _____ . (*I may have taken on
more work than I'm capable of doing.*)

12 Although it was obvious the main speaker at the conference
knew her _____ , she had such a boring voice that
most people switched off or fell asleep during her talk. (*She really
knew her subject.*)

13 If you ask me, babysitting is **money for** _____ . You get
to watch TV, eat sandwiches and drink Coke and get paid for it!
(*It's a very easy way to make money.*)

14 I'm not surprised he ended up in prison. I always thought he was
a bad _____ . (*He was a completely worthless person.*)

15 The exam was so easy. It was a **piece of** _____ ! (*It was
really easy.*)

16 My son is so neat. His bedroom's always **in** _____
order. To tell you the truth, Gunther, I'm beginning to think
there's something wrong with him! (*It's always neat and tidy.*)

17 When her mother showed her new boyfriend a photo of her in
the bath when she was five, she went **as red as a** _____ .
(*She got embarrassed and started blushing.*)

55 Idioms to do with countries and places

Solve the puzzle by filling in the missing words in the following sentences. Some are used more than once. To help you, some letters in the puzzle are given. When you have finished, the shaded squares will spell out a well-known saying.

#						
1	F	R	E	N	C	H
2				E		
3					N	
4		R				
5	N				S	T
6		M				
7			R			
8	C	V				Y
9		C	K			
10	S				H	
11					K	
12		T				
13	H					
14	W					
15	D					
16		D		N		
17			D			
18	G			N		
19			C			
20		E				
21	K					

1   He was absent without permission. He *took* _____ *leave.*

2   Although it's nice to go away on holiday, it's nice to return too. For most people *there's no place like* _____ .

3   Alison was *over the* _____ when she found out she'd got a place at Harvard University.

4   I don't understand a word of what he's saying. *It's all* _____ *to me!*

5   To take something to a place where there's a ready supply of it is to *take coals to* _____ .

6   You're abroad now. So *when in Rome, do as the* _____ *do!*

7   If my wife's father hadn't left us that money, we'd have found ourselves *in Queer* _____ *by now.*

8   His fellow workers *sent him to* _____ for working during the strike.

9   If she thinks she's going to be 'discovered' and become a rich and famous singer then I'm afraid she's *living in cloud* _____ *land!*

10 Thick mist with a light rain is often called _____ *mist.*

11 Andrea's house is *in the* _____ *of beyond.* I'd better draw you a map or you'll never find it.

12 As they were both students, they always *went* _____ when they went to a restaurant.

13 I wouldn't want to move away from Switzerland – *not for all the tea in* _____ !

14 José Escobar? Fancy meeting you here! It's certainly *a small* _____ , isn't it? What on earth are you doing in Tokyo?

15 She was very shy and always needed some _____ *courage* before she would get up and dance.

16 A period of warm weather in autumn is called *an* _____ *summer.*

17 Elliot is fast asleep – he's *in the land of* _____ !

18 We were *led up the* _____ *path* about the cost of the repairs. They turned out to be almost twice as expensive in the end.

19 He showed me a computer program he had written in Java. I didn't understand a thing. It was *double* _____ to me.

20 The money they had collected was just *a drop in the* _____ compared with what they actually needed.

21 With two best-sellers and a new book on the way, it seems *the* _____ *'s the limit* for this talented new writer.

The missing saying is:

_____

(CLUE: It takes time to change things or to make progress. You need to be patient and not get discouraged.)

French leave comes from a custom in France in the eighteenth century of leaving a party without saying goodbye to your host or hostess.
To *nod off* means to fall asleep. So if you're *in the land of Nod*, you have *nodded off!*

56 Idioms to do with crime

A Match the idioms on the left with the correct definition on the right.

1	an inside job	a	likely to steal things
2	get off scot-free	b	to put money which has been obtained illegally into legal businesses and bank accounts
3	go joyriding	c	a person who cannot be trusted
4	launder money	d	doing or about to do something wrong or illegal
5	be light-fingered	e	to steal a car and to drive it (often dangerously) just for fun
6	be on the fiddle	f	avoid being punished, although you deserve to be
7	a snake in the grass	g	a crime committed by someone connected with the place or organization where the crime took place
8	be up to no good	h	getting money dishonestly or illegally

Write your answers here:

1	2	3	4	5	6	7	8
g							

B   Say whether the idioms in the following sentences are used correctly (true) or incorrectly (false).

		True	False
1	£15 for a sandwich! That's **daylight robbery**!	✓	_____
2	The bank robbers have been finally **put behind bars**.	_____	_____
3	The thieves were **caught red-handed** as they were leaving the shop through a back window.	_____	_____
4	To **blow the whistle** is to publicly reveal something illegal or dishonest.	_____	_____
5	He was threatened with a knife. He was **ripped off**.	_____	_____
6	He's in prison. He's **doing time**.	_____	_____
7	He is in hiding from the police. He's **sailing close to the wind**.	_____	_____
8	My son is very interested in geography and is always **wheeling and dealing**.	_____	_____
9	I won't steal again! I've decided to **go straight**.	_____	_____
10	**Sharp practice** is another word for dishonesty or cheating.	_____	_____
11	The robbery happened very quickly. The thieves **pulled a fast one**.	_____	_____
12	The accountant was arrested for **cooking the books**.	_____	_____
13	He asked me to help him launder money. He asked me to **take him to the cleaners**.	_____	_____
14	Another phrase for 'do a runner' is **do a bunk**.	_____	_____

57 Idioms to do with movement and travel

Choose the word or phrase (a, b or c) which best completes the idiom in the following sentences:

1   When I offered $6 for the watch and the market trader asked for
     $10, I suggested we _____ . He agreed, and so I got it for $8!

     a) made ends meet   (b) split the difference   c) pick up the tab

     (Meaning: *We finally decided on the difference between the two prices.*)

2   Most of the beaches in Spain in August are _____ with
     tourists.

     a) tightly squeezed   b) well-oiled   c) jam-packed

     (Meaning: *The beaches are very crowded.*)

3   We've missed the last train. Let's try and _____ home.

     a) thumb a lift   b) well-oiled   c) jump on the bandwagon

     (Meaning: *Let's try and hitchhike home.*)

4   'Excuse me, where is the Tourist Information Centre?'

     'It's straight ahead. Just follow your _____ , you can't miss it!'

     a) feet   b) head   c) nose

     (Meaning: *Just keep going straight ahead.*)

5   It's getting late. I think we'd better _____ if we want to catch
     the last bus back to our boarding house.

     a) make tracks   b) hit the bottle   c) fly off the handle

     (Meaning: *We'd better leave.*)

6   I've just had a postcard from Dominic. He seems to be _____
     in Ibiza.

     a) run off his feet b) kicking up a fuss c) having the time of his life

     (Meaning: *He seems to be having a really good time.*)

7 The popular resorts are too crowded nowadays. It's better to find somewhere a bit _____ .

a) over the hill   b) off the beaten track   c) out of this world

(Meaning: *It's best to find somewhere that is not very easy to reach, that is far away from anywhere.*)

8 We're going to visit the Tower of London tomorrow. Would you like to _____ ?

a) tag along   b) hang about   c) crop up

(Meaning: *Would you like to come with us?*)

9 According to the travel brochure we read, the hotel was only _____ from Disney World.

a) a short drop   b) a close shave   c) a stone's throw

(Meaning: *It was very close to Disney World.*)

10 This two-week holiday in the Caribbean is _____ .

a) on the right track   b) just what the doctor ordered
c) made to measure

(Meaning: *It's exactly what I need at the moment.*)

11 That particular ski resort in Austria is very popular with _____ .

a) the jet set   b) high fliers   c) whizz kids

(Meaning: *It is very popular with rich and fashionable people who travel about a lot.*)

12 As the coach stopped in the car park, most of the passengers made a _____ for the nearest toilets.

a) flying visit   b) beeline   c) short cut

(Meaning: *They went quickly and directly to the nearest toilets.*)

58 Idioms as responses

Complete the dialogues below with a suitable idiomatic phrase. Choose from the following and use each phrase once only.

> a little bird told me   all ears   and pigs might fly
> better safe than sorry   have a go   I haven't a clue
> it serves him right   it's a mug's game   ~~keep your hair on~~
> mind your own business   no way   rings a bell   sleep on it
> the more the merrier   your guess is as good as mine
> you're pulling my leg

1. A: Hurry up, will you, or we'll be late!

   B: All right! _____ **Keep your hair on** _____ ! I'm coming!

   (Meaning: *Stay calm; don't get excited!*)

2. A: So are you going to take the job or not?

   B: I'm not sure. I'd like to _____
   first!

   (Meaning: *I'd like to put off making a decision until I've thought about it some more.*)

3. A: How did you find out that Rosita and I had got engaged?

   B: _____ !

   (Meaning: *You say this when you don't want to give the name of the person who told you.*)

4. A: Do you ever play the National Lottery, Jack?

   B: No, _____ ! You don't have a
   ghost of a chance of winning!

   (Meaning: *It's something only fools would get involved in as you can never win.*)

5   A: Do you think Mark and Helga will ever get married?

B: _____ ! But it's possible, I suppose.

(Meaning: *I have no idea.*)

6   A: Have you heard of Billie Redman?

B: Yes, her name _____ ! She's been on TV, hasn't she?

(Meaning: *Her name sounds familiar; I recognize the name.*)

7   A: Shall we bother with holiday insurance this time? We're only away for a week.

B: Yes, I think we should. _____ !

(Meaning: *It is better to be careful now so that nothing bad will happen later.*)

8   A: Can I borrow the car, Dad?

B: _____ ! You nearly crashed it the last time you drove it!

(Meaning: *Definitely not.*)

9   A: Jacques and Monique have split up!

B: Oh, no. I can't believe it! _____ ! They've always been so happy together.

(Meaning: *You're teasing me; you can't mean it.*)

10 A: Have you heard the latest about the new boss?

B: I'm _____ ! I love a bit of gossip!

(Meaning: *I'm listening with great interest and attention.*)

11 A: Could you help me wallpaper the bedroom?

B: I'm no expert, but I'll _____ .

(Meaning: *I'll try and do it.*)

12   A: Is it OK to bring a few friends along to the party?

     B: Yes, sure. _____ !

       (Meaning: *You use this when you tell someone you will be happy if they and others join you in something you are doing.*)

13   A: How much do you earn?

     B: _____ !

       (Meaning: *You use this phrase to tell someone that something is private and that you don't want them to ask about it.*)

14   A: He was caught stealing a car and now he's in prison.

     B: Well, _____ ! People who break the law should expect to be punished.

       (Meaning: *It's his own fault, he deserves it.*)

15   A: I'm sure Wales will qualify for the next World Cup!

     B: Yes, _____ ! Have you seen who's in their group – Germany and Russia! They haven't got a chance!

       (Meaning: *You say this when you believe that something is very unlikely to happen.*)

16   A: Do you know where Broad Street is, please?

     B: Sorry, _____ ! I've only just moved here.

       (Meaning: *I have no idea.*)

Some of the above idioms have other equivalents:
Your guess is as good as mine!   *It's anybody's guess!*
You're kidding!   *You're joking!/You're pulling my leg!*
No way!   *Over my dead body!*

59 Idioms in jokes

Complete the following jokes with a suitable idiom, making any changes that may be necessary. Choose from the following:

down in the mouth	~~fall head over heels in love~~
in (someone's) shoes	(not) have a leg to stand on
(not) stand in someone's way	pull (oneself) together
put on the shortlist	tell (someone) off

1 I once knew two acrobats who _fell head over heels in love_ .

2 When Alberto auditioned for the part of one of the dwarfs in the West End musical *Snow White and the Seven Dwarfs*, the director told him that he had been _____ .

3 'I just don't know what to do. What would *you* do if you were _____ ?'
'Polish them!'

4 *Small boy*: Please, miss, would you be angry and _____ _____ for something I didn't do?
Teacher: No, of course not.
Small boy: Oh, good! Then I can tell you that I haven't done my homework!

5 'Doctor! Doctor! I think I'm a pair of curtains!'
'Well, _____ !'

6 'Why is a dentist always unhappy?'
'Because he looks _____ !'

7 *Son*: When I grow up I'm going to drive a tank.
Father: Well, I certainly _____ !

8 When my friend's dog was faced with four trees, he _____ !

Another idiom for *pull yourself together* is *snap out of it!*
Another idiom for *tell someone off* is *give someone a piece of your mind*.

60 Just for fun 6

Complete the spiral puzzle by filling in the missing words in the sentences below. The last letter of one word is the first letter of the next. Go round the board in a clockwise direction. All the idioms are found in Tests 51–59.

1. Neil felt really happy when his doctor gave him a _____ bill of health.

2. Dillon is in the land of _____ at the moment. I'll tell him you called when he wakes up.

3. I'm not paying those prices! It's nothing but _____ robbery!

4. As we'd missed the last bus, we decided to _____ a lift home.

5   Flats in the town centre nowadays cost a _____ . I could never afford one.

6   I'm really _____ -off with my present job. I think it's time to look for another.

7   No one really understood the poem Penny read out. It was _____ Dutch to most people.

8   Watch what you say in front of Lawrence. He's all _____ !

9   She hasn't congratulated you on getting your book published because hers was turned down. It's only _____ grapes on her part.

10   They were so frightened when the earthquake started that for a minute they were _____ to the spot.

11   If I'm going to ask Rosa to marry me I'm going to need some _____ courage first.

12   I'm coming! I'm coming, William! Keep your _____ on!

13   They've got a Mercedes, a Jaguar and a BMW. They must be _____ in money.

14   He's far too old to play the lead. He's got one foot in the _____ .

15   It's hard for most students to make _____ meet.

16   Although he admitted committing the crime, he somehow managed to get off _____ -free.

17   It's late. I think it's time we made _____ .

18   It looks like rain. Take an umbrella with you. After all, better _____ than sorry.

19   Our teachers, Miss Hitchcock and Mrs Morgan, went off at the deep _____ when they found out that no one had done their homework.

20 The money we've raised so far is just a _____ in the ocean compared with what we need.

21 'Do you think I'll be a famous rock star one day?'

'And _____ might fly! You can't even sing!'

22 What's wrong Emily? You've gone as white as a _____ !

23 No, I can't lend you £50. Money doesn't grow on _____ , you know!

24 Mr Byer told me he got a set of golf clubs for a _____ at a local car boot sale.

25 'Do you think England will beat Germany tomorrow?'

'Your _____ is as good as mine!'

26 Without a new bank loan I'm going to find myself in Queer _____ .

27 'I wouldn't be married to Louis – not for all the _____ in China!' Kim told her best friend.

28 I'd like to buy a new laptop, but a decent one costs an _____ and a leg.

29 'Can I bring Jenny to the party?'

'Of course. The more the _____ !'

30 'Take these tablets and you'll be as _____ as rain in no time,' his doctor said.

31 The newsreader announced that the President's life was still hanging by a _____ .

32 Julius bought lots of things when he visited Jakarta as everything was _____ cheap compared with prices at home.

33 Her husband is doing _____ for armed robbery.

Answers

Test 1 Describing people 1

1 e	2 k	3 b	4 g
5 j	6 l	7 h	8 d
9 c	10 f	11 a	12 i

Test 2 Describing people 2

1 c	2 l	3 k	4 i
5 g	6 j	7 b	8 d
9 a	10 f	11 h	12 e

Test 3 Describing moods, states and feelings

1 down in the dumps
2 ill at ease
3 on the dole
4 bedridden
5 tongue-tied
6 peckish
7 hard of hearing
8 broke
9 off-colour
10 broken-hearted
11 laid up
12 dead beat
13 keyed up
14 scared stiff

Test 4 Describing things

A 1 few and far between
2 fishy
3 hair-raising
4 whole-hearted
5 frosty
6 long-winded
7 second-hand
8 dog-eared
9 eye-catching
B 1 long-winded
2 frosty
3 dog-eared
4 few and far between
5 fishy

Test 5 Adjective + noun combinations 1

1 b (a very severe and painful headache)
2 c (it needs to be recharged)
3 a (likes children very much)
4 b (a situation in which you only just avoid danger)
5 a (generalization)
6 c (something that you only start to like after you have tried it a few times)
7 b (a man who is quite happy being single and has no wish to get married)
8 c (something you really dislike because it annoys you)
9 b (she talked to people in an angry, unkind and criticizing way)
10 c (proper and substantial meal)
11 b (he easily loses his temper)
12 c (something that is known and understood by everyone without being formally written down)
13 a (have no idea whatsoever)
14 c (a result that can be predicted in advance)
15 b (wanting something to be true that can never be true in reality)

Test 6 Adjective + noun combinations 2

A
1 d	2 i	3 k	4 e
5 a	6 g	7 j	8 f
9 b	10 l	11 h	12 c

B 1 an old hand
2 a marked man
3 a back seat driver
4 a general dogsbody

Test 7 Adjective + noun combinations 3

1 True. (It's a quick way of getting there.)
2 False. (A dirty look is not a very pleasant or friendly one.)
3 True.
4 True.
5 False. (They would probably be pleased, as a plum job is the type of job everyone wants.)
6 False. (A tight spot is a difficult situation.)

ANSWERS

7 False. (It's a large sum of money paid to you when you leave a company.)
8 True. (If he had a job he could get a flat; if he had a flat he could get a job.)
9 True. (It's a story that's so incredible that it's hard to believe it's true.)
10 False. (A situation that has advantages and disadvantages.)
11 False. (A 'bilingual' person can speak two languages fluently; double Dutch = nonsense.)
12 True. (A long shot is something that has little chance of success.)
13 False. (It's just a quick visit – often on the way to somewhere else.)
14 True. (A sore point is a subject which annoys or upsets you.)
15 False. (Fat chance means very little chance.)

Test 8 Adjective pairs
1 worse (something must be accepted, whether the results will be good or bad)
2 surely (slowly but ably)
3 square (in a fair way)
4 alive (be very healthy and active)
5 sound (safe, unharmed)
6 thin (in spite of any difficulties or problems)
7 white (in writing)
8 dry (to have succeeded in doing something)
9 early (very early)
10 void (not valid)
11 less (almost)
12 easy (relaxed, friendly, without many rules)
13 tired (thoroughly bored or annoyed with someone/something)
14 low (everywhere)
15 fast (fixed, that cannot be changed)
16 sweet (not taking a long time and less boring or unpleasant than you expected)

17 dried (settled, decided)
18 spick (very neat, clean and tidy)

Test 9 Idioms using common adjectives
1 j (be out of favour with someone)
2 e (praise someone or suggest them for a particular job)
3 m (be too proud of yourself)
4 g (ignore someone)
5 b (waste your time or effort doing something)
6 l (for ever)
7 o (short of money)
8 i (pretend to be less interested in someone or something than you really are)
9 a (to be punished for something you have done wrong)
10 n (you say this when something must be done without delay)
11 d (become angry or excited)
12 h (be successful, make a good career for yourself)
13 c (get into trouble)
14 k (terminate something, like a holiday sooner than expected)
15 f (not very numerous; in short supply)

Test 10 Just for fun 1
Across:
2 fast, 4 hot, 5 soft, 7 rough, 8 hair, 10 pet, 11 tongue, 12 big, 13 alive, 15 nosy, 16 backseat, 20 hen, 22 wet, 23 blanket, 24 horse, 25 colour.
Down:
1 sharp, 2 fishy, 3 vicious, 6 thin, 9 handshake, 10 pig, 11 thick, 12 bright, 14 eye, 17 collar, 18 skinny, 19 tooth, 21 null, 22 word.

Test 11 Types of people 1
1 e	2 k	3 h	4 j
5 g	6 a	7 d	8 i
9 b	10 l	11 c	12 f

Test 12 Types of people 2

an early bird 2 (someone who always gets up very early in the morning)

a guinea pig 10 (a person who is used as a subject in medical or other experiments)

a jailbird 3 (someone who is constantly in and out of prison)

a killjoy 5 (a person who intentionally spoils the pleasure of other people)

a night owl 1 (someone who likes to stay up at night)

a nosy parker 6 (a person who always wants to know or find out about other people's private lives)

a road hog 11 (a very selfish and careless driver)

a rolling stone 8 (someone who can't settle down and goes from job to job, place to place)

a scapegoat 4 (someone who is unfairly blamed or punished for the mistakes of others, usually because people are very angry and want to see someone blamed or punished)

a skinflint 9 (someone who is mean and miserly and hates spending or giving money away)

a troublemaker 12 (a person who regularly causes trouble, especially by making others feel discontented)

a white-collar worker 7 (a worker who does an office job)

Test 13 Nouns from phrasal verbs

1 b	2 m	3 a	4 o
5 e	6 k	7 c	8 f
9 h	10 i	11 n	12 g
13 d	14 j	15 l	

Test 14 Single nouns

A	1 j	2 g	3 k	4 n
	5 b	6 h	7 d	8 a
	9 m	10 c	11 i	12 f
	13 l	14 e		

B 1 an eyesore
   2 a catnap
   3 a blackout
   4 a windfall

Test 15 Noun phrases 1

1 c	2 a	3 b	4 c
5 b	6 c	7 b	8 a
9 c	10 c	11 b	12 b
13 a	14 b	15 c	

Test 16 Noun phrases 2

1 b	2 c	3 b	4 a
5 c	6 c	7 b	8 a
9 b	10 b	11 c	12 c
13 b	14 c	15 c	

Test 17 Noun pairs

1 fingers and thumbs (very clumsy)
2 nook and cranny (look everywhere)
3 life and soul (the person who brings fun and excitement to a social gathering, e.g. a party)
4 wear and tear (the amount of damage you can expect to carpets, furniture, etc. through daily use)
5 hustle and bustle (busy and noisy activity)
6 skin and bone (very thin)
7 cock and bull (a story or excuse that is really silly and unbelievable, but told as though it were true)
8 hand in glove (working very closely with someone else, especially in something that is bad or illegal)
9 flesh and blood (family member, relative)
10 back to front (wearing something the wrong way round)
11 pros and cons (the advantages and disadvantages of something)
12 fun and games (pleasurable, playful activities)
13 tooth and nail (fight or argue fiercely)
14 head and shoulders (be much better at something than everyone else)
15 ups and downs (good and bad moments)

Test 18 Idioms using common nouns 1
be at the end of your tether 4 (be so worried, tired, etc. that you feel you can no longer deal with a difficult or upsetting situation)
be at a loose end 15 (to have spare time but no idea what to do with it)
get hold of the wrong end of the stick 7 (completely misunderstand something)
It's not the end of the world! 13 (It won't cause any serious problems. Something will turn up!)
make ends meet 10 (manage on the money you earn; manage to survive with very little money)
drop someone a line 3 (write a letter to someone)
read between the lines 1 (to guess someone's real feelings from what they say or write)
toe the line 6 (behave as you ought to; obey orders; do as you are told)
a weight off your mind 12 (a great relief; the end of a worrying or anxious time)
can't make up your mind 9 (unable to decide)
give someone a piece of your mind 2 (tell someone exactly what you think of his/her behaviour)
slip your mind 14 (forget something)
at point blank range 5 (from a very close distance)
I take your point! 11 (I understand and agree with you)
What's the point? 8 (What is the use?)

Test 19 Idioms using common nouns 2
1 True.
2 False. (This has nothing to do with directions. You are in a difficult situation and don't know who to turn to for help.)
3 False. (It is the opposite. You are having a wonderful time.)
4 True.
5 True.

6 False. (A person who doesn't mince his/her words speaks clearly and directly, even if it upsets people.)
7 True.
8 False. (It has nothing to do with weather. It means to see how a situation is developing before making a decision about it.)
9 False. (To arrive in next to no time is to arrive very quickly indeed.)
10 True. (You use this phrase when you are certain something will happen in the future.)
11 False. (They may be able to march in time, however, to arrive in good time means to arrive well before the time something is due to start.)
12 True. (It means we have known each other for a very long time.)
13 False. (It's far from main roads and other people.)
14 True. (It means 'Don't say a word!')
15 True. (They only just arrived in time.)
16 False. (To take the words from someone's mouth is to say what he was about to say or was thinking.)
17 True. (It means doing something while you are waiting for time to pass.)

Test 20 Just for fun 2

1	blackleg	11	stick
2	early	12	throw
3	outbreak	13	gift
4	brainwave	14	skinflint
5	storm	15	kill
6	thumbs	16	scapegoat
7	child	17	loose
8	downpour	18	nick
9	words	19	nook
10	ends	20	bottleneck

The missing proverb is: Great minds think alike.

Test 21　Verb + noun collocations

1　permission, the way
2　your leg, the ice (*break the ice* = make people who haven't met before feel more relaxed with each other)
3　a cold, fire
4　a conclusion, the curtains (*draw the curtains* = pull them together)
5　thanks, the impression
6　the fort, the line (*hold the fort* = be responsible for looking after something while the person usually responsible is away; *hold the line* = ask the person on the telephone to wait for a while)
7　face, your temper (*lose face* = be humiliated; *lose your temper* = become angry)
8　a living, a speech (*make a living* = earn money to live on)
9　attention, someone a compliment
10　between the lines, someone's palm

Test 22　Verb + noun combinations 1

1　the time
2　the handle
　　(*call someone's bluff* = tell someone to do what they threaten because you don't really think they will do it; *call the shots* = be in control of what is happening)
3　a speech (= make a speech)
　　(*do wonders* = be very effective in solving a problem; *do the trick* = solve a problem; provide what is needed)
4　the bacon
　　(*get the sack* = be dismissed from your job)
5　one's goat
　　(*go public* = tell everyone about something that was secret)
6　pieces
　　(*have kittens* = be very anxious or upset about something)
7　the boat
　　(*hit the sack* = go to bed; *hit the jackpot* = win the big prize)

8　the traffic
　　(*jump the gun* = start doing something too soon, especially without thinking about it properly; *jump the queue* = to go in front of people in a queue)
9　steam
　　(*make a bomb* = make a lot of money; *make a move* = leave)
10　the roof
　　(*play second fiddle* = be in a lower position or rank than someone else; *play the fool* = act in a foolish, silly way)
11　the beans
　　(*pull strings* = use your influence with important people in order to get what you want or help someone else; *pull one's weight* = do one's full share of work)
12　reason
　　(*run riot* = behave in a violent, noisy and uncontrolled way; *run the gauntlet* = to deal with a lot of people who are criticizing or attacking you)
13　the ropes
　　(*see the sights* = see famous and interesting places as a tourist)
14　the bucket
　　(*take the plunge* = finally decide to do something important or difficult you have been thinking about doing for a long time; *take the biscuit* = to be the most surprising, annoying, etc. thing you have ever heard)
15　the fence
　　(*throw a fit* = be very angry or shocked)

Test 23　Verb + noun combinations 2

1　go halves
2　cook the books
3　pop the question
4　surf the net
5　bury the hatchet
6　talk shop
7　stretch your legs
8　drop a clanger
9　kick the bucket

10 sit on the fence
11 lose your nerve
12 spill the beans
13 fly off the handle
14 smell a rat

Test 24 Idioms using *give* and *take*

A 1 e
   2 g
   3 f
   4 c
   5 a
   6 h
   7 d
   8 b

B

1 The two boys *took to their heels* when the farmer chased them.
2 Let's check the Internet to see if there are any last minute cheap holidays going somewhere tomorrow. It doesn't matter where – we'll just *take pot luck*.
3 Nimah tends to exaggerate a lot. If I were you *I'd take everything he says with a pinch of salt.*
4 The new British boy band has *taken America by storm*.
5 I told him he couldn't borrow my new laptop, but he kept on asking anyway. He just *wouldn't take no for an answer*.
6 It was only when he got home after the car boot sale that he found out the TV didn't work. The woman he had bought it from had *taken him for a ride*.
7 His doctor told him to *take things easy* for a while.
8 Just because someone has stolen your mobile phone, there's no need to *take it out on me*. It wasn't my fault!
9 $10,000 – and that's my final offer! *Take it or leave it.*
10 There was an expectant hush as the guest speaker *took the floor*.
11 They told everyone that their wedding would *take place* at St Mary's church on 18th September.

Test 25 Idioms using *break*, *have* and *make*

A

BREAK

even (if a company breaks even, it makes neither a profit nor a loss)
one's word (to break a promise)
someone's heart (to make someone really sad and heartbroken)
the back of something (to succeed in dealing with the worst part of a problem or piece of work)
the news (to say or tell someone what has happened)

HAVE

a bee in one's bonnet (to have a fixed idea or obsession about something)
a bone to pick with someone (have a difference to settle)
a chip on one's shoulder (to easily become offended or angry because you think you have been treated unfairly in the past)
a good time (to enjoy yourself)
a lump in one's throat (to feel like crying)

MAKE

a mountain out of a molehill (to make a lot of fuss about nothing)
a scene (to make a fuss, quarrel)
fun of someone (to laugh or make jokes about someone)
one's blood boil (to make one angry)
short work of something (to do a job quickly)

B

1 making a mountain out of a molehill
2 a bee in his bonnet
3 break even
4 a bone to pick
5 makes my blood boil
6 break the news
7 making a scene
8 broke André's heart
9 make fun of
10 had a chip on her shoulder

Test 26 Idioms using *bring*, *come* and *go*

1 b
2 i
3 j
4 d
5 a
6 c
7 m
8 e
9 n
10 h
11 l
12 g
13 k
14 f

Test 27 Idioms using *get* and *keep*

1 True.
2 False. (If someone gets on your nerves they annoy or irritate you.)
3 True. (It means to keep in contact with them.)
4 True. (To get the hang of something is to get used to doing it.)
5 False. (It means they are in a bad mood.)
6 True.
7 True. (To keep a stiff upper lip is to show no emotion, especially in a crisis.)
8 False. (To keep your head above water is to keep out of debt, to avoid money problems.)
9 True. (You keep your fingers crossed to bring someone good luck.)
10 True. (It means you finally talked about a problem that has been troubling you.)
11 False. (It means to hear a rumour about something.)
12 False. (It means to keep a secret.)
13 True.
14 False. (Keep someone in the dark is not to tell someone about something.)
15 False. (You would hardly feel proud if you were dismissed from your job.)
16 True.

Test 28 Idioms using *pull*, *put* and *turn*

A 1 e
2 h
3 f
4 c
5 a
6 g
7 d
8 b

B
1 His daughter asked to go to an all-night party, but *he put his foot down* and told her she would have to be home by midnight.
2 They were going to build the highest skyscraper in the world in a bid to *put their city on the map*.
3 It was his views on whale hunting that really *put the cat among the pigeons*.
4 He saw the young boy take the bar of chocolate without paying for it, but he decided to *turn a blind eye to it*.
5 Ask your uncle to try and *pull strings* to get you the job.
6 I'm too smart for you! You can't *pull the wool over my eyes!*
7 When he noticed that both his wife and best friend always went out alone the same evenings every week, he *put two and two together* and came to the conclusion that they were having an affair.
8 Tell your daughter you need the car this weekend – that'll *put a spoke in her wheel*.

Test 29 Idioms using various verbs

1 a (To 'bury the hatchet' means to make peace after quarrelling.)
2 b (To 'bark up the wrong tree' is to make a mistake, have the wrong idea about something.)
3 b (To 'lead someone up the garden path' is to trick or deceive them.)
4 a (To 'go like a bomb' is to move very fast or sell extremely well.)

5 b (To 'beat about the bush' is to avoid saying directly what you mean.)

6 c (To 'miss the boat' is to miss an opportunity.)

7 c (To be 'pipped at the post' is to be beaten at the last minute in a race.)

8 b (To 'blow your own trumpet' is to boast about your ability or things you have done.)

9 a (To 'be like two peas in a pod' is to be identical.)

10 c (To 'get something for a song' is to get it very cheaply.)

11 a (To 'throw in the towel' is to surrender.)

12 b (To 'be a flash in the pan' is to be fashionable or popular for just a short time.)

13 a (To 'skate on thin ice' is to be in a risky or dangerous position.)

14 c (To 'give someone a piece of your mind' is to speak angrily and bluntly to them.)

15 c (To 'be in the doghouse' is to be out of favour with someone.)

16 b (If something 'drives you up the wall' it irritates and annoys you.)

Test 30 Just for fun 3
Across:
1 luck, 5 bomb, 7 blind, 9 bluff, 10 socks, 13 hat, 17 lines, 18 slip, 19 bee, 20 bust, 22 raining, 24 wrong, 25 books.

Down:
2 chip, 3 boil, 4 stiff, 5 beans, 6 move, 7 bucket, 8 Dutch, 9 barking, 10 shoulder, 11 chest, 12 pulling, 14 throat, 15 legs, 16 surfing, 21 sack, 23 ice.

Test 31 Idioms using *at*
1 at a rough guess
2 at loggerheads
3 at large
4 at (such) short notice
5 at the drop of a hat
6 at a loss
7 at the eleventh hour
8 at a pinch
9 at will
10 at death's door
11 at the crack of dawn
12 at sixes and sevens
13 at a standstill
14 at her wits' end
15 at a stretch

Test 32 Idioms using *by* and *for*
1 The football hooligans admitted to smashing shop windows just **for kicks**.

2 If taxes continue to rise, I shall leave this country **for good**.

3 Do you like my ring? I saw it quite **by chance** in the window of an antique shop while I was shopping in the Old Town.

4 This piano was a present from my grandmother and I wouldn't part with it **for love or money**.

5 The government has decided to drop its plans to raise the school leaving age to eighteen – at least **for the time being**.

6 His name was Benjamin, but he was called Ben **for short**.

7 The car swerved to avoid a cyclist and missed a pedestrian **by a hair's breadth**.

8 Mr Wilson's **for the high jump**. He's been caught fiddling the accounts.

9 Probably the only really effective way of learning prepositions is to learn them **by heart**.

10 He can't read a note of music – he plays everything **by ear**.

11 It is **by no means** uncommon for squirrels to bury nuts in autumn.
12 I was rushing this morning and put my jumper on back to front **by mistake**./I was rushing this morning and **by mistake** I put my jumper on back to front.

Test 33 Idioms using *in*
1 long run (in the end; over a long period of time)
2 dark (without being told; not knowing what is happening, kept secret)
3 succession (happening one after the other without a break in between)
4 cold blood (deliberately and cruelly)
5 nutshell (briefly and clearly)
6 red (in debt, owing the bank money)
7 season (the time when plants, fruit are normally ripe)
8 dribs and drabs (in small irregular numbers over a period of time)
9 mint condition (in perfect condition; looking new)
10 good shape (in good condition; fit)
11 flash (very quickly)
12 stitches (laugh uncontrollably)
13 flesh (to see or meet someone you had only previously seen on television, in pictures, etc.)
14 turns (to share, each person doing it alternately)
15 common (having the same interests, attitudes, etc.)
16 deep water (in serious trouble)
17 broad daylight (happening in the daylight rather than at night)
18 cold sweat (to feel frightened)
19 vain (without any success)
20 doldrums (feeling sad and depressed)

Test 34 Idioms using *on* and *off*
1 e (without planning beforehand)
2 h (this is the opposite of being measured up for a dress, jacket, etc.; off the peg clothes usually come in standard sizes only)

3 k (very nervous, anxious)
4 j (irregularly; from time to time)
5 f (at 8.30 exactly)
6 c (you hope something will happen, even though it is not likely)
7 i (fleeing from the police)
8 l (you say this when you know something, but can't quite remember it at the time you are speaking)
9 g (not working, the opposite of 'on duty')
10 d (be very alert)
11 b (have more than enough to do)
12 a (unofficial; not for publication)

Test 35 Idioms using *out of*
1 True. (Unable to breathe easily because of running, working hard, etc.)
2 True. (You haven't done it for a long time.)
3 False. (Something that is out of place is not in the correct position.)
4 True. (It got out of control.)
5 True.(They have stopped printing new copies of it.)
6 False. (To be out of condition is to be unfit.)
7 True. (It was too difficult to handle.)
8 False. (An out of tune voice would hardly be lovely!)
9 False. (You would not be pleased if you have lost money over something!)
10 True.
11 True. (It was unexpected.)
12 True. (If you were feeling slightly ill.)
13 False. (To be out of the running is to be no longer in a competition, no longer have a chance of winning.)
14 True. (Not allowed to go there.)
15 False. (Used when you say that there are likely to be more difficulties before things improve.)
16 True. (So they can't reach or get at them.)

Test 36 Idioms using prepositions and particles

1 above board (honest)
2 round the bend (crazy)
3 to my face (= directly) behind my back (in a sly, underhand way)
4 on principle (as a matter of principle)
5 Between you, me and the gatepost (what I am saying is in strict confidence)
6 At this rate (if we continue at the same speed as before)
7 off the cuff (without preparing it)
8 on edge (tense and nervous)
9 be in her shoes (to actually be in that person's position or situation)
10 up to my ears in work (be very busy)
11 letting off steam (getting rid of feelings of aggression)
12 from scratch (from the beginning)
13 with baited breath (nervously and anxiously)
14 at all hours (all the time, both morning and night)
15 down the drain (wasted)
16 on account of (because of)

Test 37 Idioms using various prepositions 1

1 d (He's very talented. He plays the trumpet by ear, i.e. from memory rather than by reading music.)
2 f (The party was in full swing when they arrived, i.e. very lively, at its most active.)
3 l (The restaurant was out of this world, i.e. so good and quite unlike anything else you have ever experienced.)
4 a (The numbers are chosen at random, i.e. by chance, not in any set order.)
5 h (Promise me you'll keep in touch always, i.e. in contact with each other.)
6 b (He's still behind bars, i.e. in prison.)
7 j (Help! Help! My house is on fire!, i.e. it is burning.)
8 c (They're a bit behind the times, i.e. old-fashioned.)
9 e (After twenty-five years of farming, I feel I'm in a rut, i.e. be in a situation that never changes, so that you feel bored.)
10 g (She loves being in the limelight, i.e. in the public eye and the centre of attention.)
11 i (Our house is off the beaten track, i.e. out of the way; away from towns, villages; in a lonely place.)
12 k (Your coffee machine seems to be out of order, i.e. broken, not working.)

Test 38 Idioms using various prepositions 2

1 over the moon (really happy)
2 up with the lark (got up very early)
3 down in the dumps (sad, depressed, feeling low)
4 off her head (mad, crazy)
5 by word of mouth (by people telling each other about something rather than through advertising or other printed information)
6 by the skin of her teeth (she had a narrow escape, a close shave)
7 up in arms (very angry and protesting strongly about something)
8 under your hat (keep quiet about)
9 fallen off the back of a lorry (they are stolen goods)
10 under the weather (slightly ill, unwell)
11 in his birthday suit (naked)
12 up to scratch (she wasn't good enough)

Test 39 Idioms using various prepositions 3

1 a	2 c	3 b	4 a
5 b	6 c	7 b	8 c
9 c	10 a	11 b	12 c
13 a	14 b	15 c	

Test 40 Just for fun 4

Across:

1 shoes, 2 kicks, 6 hair, 7 tongue,
8 plate, 10 standstill, 13 mint, 15 spur,
18 drain, 19 flesh, 20 steam, 21 carpet,
23 stitches, 27 blood, 29 lorry,
30 minds, 31 nutshell, 32 pinch.

Down:

1 sorts, 3 cuff, 4 shoestring, 5 toes,
9 thumb, 11 loggerheads, 12 mouth,
14 track, 15 street, 16 touch, 17 jump,
18 depth, 22 random, 24 chance,
25 moon, 26 flying, 27 blue, 28 dawn.

Test 41 Parts of the body idioms 1

1	head	9	teeth
2	tongue-in-cheek	10	chin
3	ears	11	nose
4	tooth	12	face
5	ear	13	tongue
6	brain	14	hair
7	lips	15	eye
8	eyes		

Test 42 Parts of the body idioms 2

1 True.
2 False. (If something makes your flesh creep it makes you really frightened.)
3 False. (It should be 'hand and foot'.)
4 False. (It should be 'put your feet up'.)
5 True.
6 False. (If you have your heart in your mouth, you are terrified.)
7 True.
8 True. (It means to become discouraged.)
9 False. (To have a finger in every pie is to be involved in many activities and to have influence over them.)
10 False. (To read someone's palm is to tell their fortune. To grease someone's palm is to offer them a bribe.)
11 True.

12 False. (To give someone the elbow is to end a relationship with someone.)
13 True.
14 True.
15 False. (If you have your back to the wall you are really struggling against difficulties.)
16 True.
17 False. (If you eat your heart out you are unhappy about something or someone and want them very much.)
18 False. (You would probably kick yourself, though. To kick your heels is to hang about or waste time waiting for something.)
19 True. (It had three different owners.)
20 True.
21 False. (You wouldn't be happy if someone told you how angry they were with you!)
22 True.
23 True.

The missing idiom is: Blood is thicker than water.

Test 43 Parts of the body idioms 3

1 c	2 f	3 j	4 n
5 i	6 o	7 b	8 m
9 h	10 l	11 g	12 d
13 e	14 k	15 a	

Test 44 Colour idioms

A	1 g	2 c	3 f	4 e
	5 a	6 h	7 b	8 d

B	1	green	9 black … blue
	2	black	10 green
	3	green	11 red
	4	blue	12 black
	5	red	13 red
	6	yellow	14 black
	7	red	15 blue
	8	pink	16 red

Test 45 Animal idioms 1

1 b	2 a	3 c	4 c
5 b	6 a	7 c	8 c
9 c	10 b	11 a	12 c
13 b	14 b	15 a	

Test 46 Animal idioms 2

1 b	2 a	3 c	4 b
5 a	6 b	7 c	8 c
9 b	10 a	11 c	12 b
13 a	14 b	15 b	16 c

Test 47 Idioms of comparison 1

1 b (calm and relaxed, especially in dangerous situations)
2 a (completely dead)
3 c (stone deaf; unable to hear a thing)
4 b (completely different)
5 c (very fit and healthy)
6 c (very gentle)
7 c (very well behaved)
8 a (hard and ruthless; physically and mentally tough)
9 b (very heavy)
10 b (very keen or enthusiastic)
11 c (actually there; present in person)
12 a (very light)
13 b (very old)
14 c (very obvious; clearly evident)
15 c (completely well, usually after an illness)
16 b (absolutely safe; secure and stable; not likely to collapse)
17 b (very sick or unwell)
18 a (very strong)
19 c (very friendly; strongly bonded together in friendship)
20 b (very thin)

Test 48 Idioms of comparison 2

1 15 a brick wall (You don't get anywhere!)
2 7 a ton of bricks (She'll punish you severely.)
3 9 a fish out of water (She felt out of place.)
4 12 a horse (He has a huge appetite.)
5 8 a glove (It fits perfectly.)
6 14 a house on fire (They got on really well.)
7 11 a light (She fell asleep immediately.)
8 4 a sieve (He's got a terrible memory.)
9 16 the back of my hand (I know it really well.)
10 18 hot cakes (It's selling quickly in large numbers.)
11 5 a leaf (She was trembling with fear.)
12 1 a log (He slept very heavily.)
13 17 a chimney (She's a very heavy smoker.)
14 13 wildfire (It spread quickly.)
15 3 a sore thumb (It will be very noticeable and out of place.)
16 6 a duck to water (She took to it really well.)
17 10 dirt (He treated her really badly.)
18 2 a bomb (It goes really fast.)

Test 49 Proverbs

A

1 Beggars can't be choosers. (If you are in need, you can't have what you want – you have to accept what is given to you.)
2 Better late than never. (It is preferable that something should happen late than not at all.)
3 Still waters run deep. (Reserved, quiet people often have deep feelings.)
4 Let sleeping dogs lie. (To not talk about things which have caused problems in the past; to leave a situation as it is rather than change it, in case by doing so you cause problems.)
5 Look before you leap.(You say this to advise someone to think about possible problems before doing something.)
6 First come, first served. (The people who ask for something first will be the ones who get it when there is not enough to go around.)
7 Nothing ventured, nothing gained. (You can't achieve anything without taking risks.)
8 No smoke without fire. (There is nearly always a basis for a rumour, no matter how untrue it appears.)

B

1 Actions speak louder than words. (What people do is more important and effective than what they say; people judge you on what you do rather than on what you say.)

2 Don't count your chickens before they're hatched. (You should wait until a good thing you are expecting has actually happened before making plans about it.)

3 Strike while the iron is hot. (Do something immediately, while you have a very good chance of success.)

4 Once bitten, twice shy. (If something you have done has turned out badly, then you are unlikely to try it again.)

5 Make hay while the sun shines. (Make use of an opportunity while it is available. Similar to strike while the iron is hot.)

6 One good turn deserves another. (If someone does something nice for you, then in return you should do something nice for them.)

7 A miss is as good as a mile. (Failing to do something when you almost succeeded is really no better than failing badly.)

8 Too many cooks spoil the broth. (If too many people try to work on the same piece of work then the chances are they will spoil it or do a very bad job; too many people trying to do the same job will get in each other's way.)

9 A bird in the hand is worth two in the bush. (It is not worth giving up something you already have for only the possibility of getting something better.)

10 Where there's a will there's a way. (If you want something badly enough, you will find a way of getting or achieving it.)

Test 50 Just for fun 5
(Suggestions: other wording variations are possible)

1 make a pig of yourself
2 the rat race
3 get something straight from the horse's mouth
4 look before you leap
5 feel that your ears are burning
6 fight tooth and nail
7 have a finger in every pie
8 a hen party
9 stick your neck out
10 keep your head above water
11 pick someone's brain
12 my lips are sealed
13 have a face as long as a fiddle
14 catch someone's eye
15 as strong as a horse

Test 51 Idioms to do with health and illness

Across:
1 fit, **4** rain, **5** run, **6** picture, **8** clean, **9** death, **11** right, **13** strong, **15** about, **16** legs, **17** thread.

Down:
2 turn, **3** weather, **5** recharge, **6** par, **7** catch, **10** sorts, **12** grave, **14** rest.

Test 52 Idioms to do with money

1 b ('In the doldrums' means you are sad and depressed. The other two mean not having much money.)

2 c ('In a flap' means you are excited, worried or worked up about something.)

3 b ('on the up and up' is becoming more successful financially)

4 c ('Split the difference' means to agree on an amount that is exactly between two amounts that have been mentioned; a = it's free; b = we share the bill 50–50.)

5 a ('At sixes and sevens' is to be disorganised and confused; b = finding things tough financially; c = to have just enough money to live on and no extra.)

6 b ('Pin money' is a small amount of money that you can spend on yourself; a = money to keep quiet, c = given a bribe.)

7 b (To be 'cheap at the price' means that something is so good that the price is unimportant.)

8 c (To be 'in the black' is the opposite of being in the red, which means you have money rather than are in debt.)

9 a (To do things 'on a shoestring' is to do them very cheaply.)

10 c (To 'hit the roof' is to lose your temper and become very angry; a and b both mean he made a lot of money.)

11 b (To 'take someone to the cleaners' means to cheat someone out of all their money or possessions; a = Let's all give him some money for a present, c = a collection for him.)

12 a (To 'hit the jackpot' is to win the big prize, b and c both mean to pay the bill.)

13 c (To 'spend a penny' means to go to the toilet; a = You should be careful about how much money you spend because there is only a limited amount, b = I haven't got money to spare.)

14 a (To 'spend money like water' means to spend a lot of money as though there was no end to it; b and c both mean the goods cost more than they were really worth.)

15 b ('To hold the purse strings' is to control the money in a family or business; a = to have problems with money because you are earning less than before, c = having to get used to less money to spend than usual.)

Test 53 Idioms to do with emotions

Feeling happy
be as pleased as Punch (be really pleased)
be in seventh heaven (be extremely happy)
be on top of the world (be really happy)
be thrilled to bits (be very happy and excited)

Feeling sad/fed up
be as miserable as sin (be extremely sad)
be browned-off (be bored)
be downhearted (feel sad)
have a long face (look unhappy)

Feeling frightened/shocked
be in a cold sweat (be in a state of shock or fear)
be rooted to the spot (be unable to move through fear)
be scared to death (be extremely frightened)
go as white as a sheet (go pale through fear or shock)

Feeling worried/anxious/nervous
be keyed up (be excited, tense)
be like a cat on hot bricks (feeling nervous and unable to stand still)
be on tenterhooks (be uncertain and anxious about what is going to happen)
have something on one's mind (have a problem that is worrying you)

Feeling confused/uncertain
be all at sea (be puzzled and bewildered)
be at sixes and sevens (be uncertain and confused)
be out of one's depth (be in a situation which is difficult for you to cope with, or where you do not understand what is happening)
not knowing whether you're coming or going (be totally confused)

Feeling angry
be hopping mad (be really angry)
be hot under the collar (be annoyed and/or embarrassed)
go off at the deep end (lose your temper; become very angry)
go spare (lose your temper; become very angry)

Feeling quarrelsome/unfriendly
avoid someone like the plague (avoid someone completely)
cut someone down to size (to reduce someone's sense of their own importance)
have a go at someone (to criticize someone angrily)
tear someone off a strip (to speak angrily to someone because they have done something wrong)

Feeling surprised
be gobsmacked (be very surprised)
not believe one's eyes (find it hard to believe something you have seen because it is so surprising)
That's a turn-up for the books! (something you say when something surprising happens)
You could have knocked me down with a feather! (something you say to emphasize how surprised you were when you heard something)

Test 54 Idioms to do with food
1	cup of tea	11	chew
2	butter	12	onions
3	grapes	13	jam
4	bananas	14	egg
5	picnic	15	cake
6	hot cakes	16	apple-pie
7	apple	17	beetroot
8	pie		
9	bacon		
10	cauliflower		

Test 55 Idioms to do with countries and places
1 French (To 'take French leave' is to be absent without permission. It is rather old-fashioned nowadays.)

2 home (Home is the best place to be.)
3 moon ('Over the moon' means you are very happy.)
4 Greek ('It's all Greek to me' means it's too hard to understand.)
5 Newcastle
6 Romans ('When in Rome, do as the Romans do' is a saying meaning that you are wise to follow the customs of the country or place in which you find yourself.)
7 street (To be 'in Queer Street' is to be in difficulties – especially to be in debt or in financial difficulties.)
8 Coventry (If you 'send someone to Coventry' you refuse to speak to them because of something bad or wrong they have done.)
9 cuckoo (To 'live in cloud cuckoo land' means to be ignorant of reality, to live in a totally unrealistic world.)
10 Scotch
11 back (If you live in the 'back of beyond' you live miles away from anywhere.)
12 Dutch (To 'go Dutch' is to share the expenses, especially at a restaurant.)
13 China ('Not for all the tea in China' is used to emphasize that you would not do something, no matter what.)
14 world ('It's a small world' is an expression you use to show your surprise at the coincidence of meeting someone unexpectedly somewhere.)
15 Dutch ('Dutch courage' is the courage you get from drinking alcohol.)
16 Indian
17 Nod (To be 'in the land of Nod' means to be asleep.)
18 garden (To 'lead someone up the garden path' is to deceive them.)
19 Dutch (If something is 'double Dutch' to you, it means you don't understand it.)

20 ocean ('A drop in the ocean' is just a small amount of what is needed.)

21 sky ('The sky's the limit' means there is no upper limit to the amount of money that can be spent or to the things that can be achieved.)

The missing saying is: Rome was not built in a day.

Test 56 Idioms to do with crime

A 1 g   2 f   3 e   4 b
   5 a   6 h   7 c   8 d

B
1 True. (It cost far more than it should.)
2 True. (They were finally sent to prison.)
3 True. (They were caught in the act of stealing.)
4 True.
5 False. (To be 'ripped off' is to be cheated.)
6 True.
7 False. ('Sailing close to the wind' means knowingly taking a chance or a risk.)
8 False. ('Wheeling and dealing' is making clever, often dishonest or illegal, business deals.)
9 True. (I've decided to lead an honest life.)
10 True.
11 False. (To 'pull a fast one' means to deceive someone.)
12 True. (He was trying to falsify the bookkeeping in order to steal money.)
13 False. (If you 'take someone to the cleaners' you steal all their money or possessions.)
14 True.

Test 57 Idioms to do with movement and travel

1 b   2 c   3 a   4 c
5 a   6 c   7 b   8 a
9 c   10 b   11 a   12 b

Test 58 Idioms as responses

1 Keep your hair on!
2 sleep on it
3 A little bird told me!
4 it's a mug's game
5 Your guess is as good as mine!
6 rings a bell
7 Better safe than sorry!
8 No way!
9 You're pulling my leg!
10 all ears
11 have a go
12 The more the merrier!
13 Mind your own business!
14 it serves him right
15 and pigs might fly!
16 I haven't a clue!

Test 59 Idioms in jokes

1 fell head over heels in love (They fell totally in love. Joke explanation: acrobats do cartwheels, etc. so turn head over heels.)
2 put on the shortlist (Put on a final shorter list of people to be selected for a job. Joke explanation: dwarfs are very short people.)
3 in my shoes (If you were in my position. Joke explanation: literally polish the other person's shoes.)
4 tell me off (reprimand me)
5 pull yourself together (Force yourself to stop behaving in a negative way; to regain your self-control. Joke explanation: you pull curtains together when you want to close them.)
6 down in the mouth (sad, depressed. Joke explanation: a dentist has to look deep inside a patient's mouth.)

7 won't stand in your way (not try to stop someone from doing something. Joke explanation: he literally won't stand in front of a tank!)

8 didn't have a leg to stand on (be in a position where you cannot prove or support what you say. Joke explanation: a dog lifts one leg when it pees against a tree. If there were four trees and it lifted all four legs, it would fall over.)

Test 60 Just for fun 6

1	clean	18	safe
2	Nod	19	end
3	daylight	20	drop
4	thumb	21	pigs
5	bomb	22	sheet
6	browned	23	trees
7	double	24	song
8	ears	25	guess
9	sour	26	Street
10	rooted	27	tea
11	Dutch	28	arm
12	hair	29	merrier
13	rolling	30	right
14	grave	31	thread
15	ends	32	dirt
16	scot	33	time
17	tracks		

Test Your way to success in English
Test Your Vocabulary

0582 45166 3

0582 45167 1

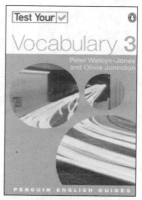

0582 45168 X

0582 45169 8

0582 45170 1

Test Your way to success in English

Test Your Professional English

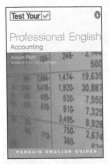

0582 45163 9

0582 45148 5

0582 45149 3

0582 45160 4

0582 45161 2

0582 46898 1

0582 46897 3

0582 45150 7

0582 45147 7

0582 45162 0